SCANNERS
A VHF/UHF Listener's Guide

Dedicated to my family

SCANNERS
A VHF/UHF Listener's Guide

Peter Rouse GU1DKD

ARGUS BOOKS

Argus Books
Argus House
Boundary Way
Hemel Hempstead
Herts HP2 7ST

© Peter Rouse, 1986
Second Edition 1987
Reprinted 1988 (twice)
Reprinted 1989 (twice)
Third Edition 1989
Reprinted 1990 (fourth impression)
Reprinted 1991

ISBN 1 85486 006 2

Phototypesetting by "The Works", Exeter, Devon
Printed and bound by Whitstable Litho Printers Ltd.,
Whitstable, Kent.

Contents

Acknowledgements

Putting together a book that contains such a vast range of information requires considerable help from many people. It would be impossible for me to name them all and indeed I suspect some would not care to be named.

Several individuals and organisations have provided essential help with information, photographs and artwork and they are:

Eric le Cornu, Richard Bird (Links Communications), Graham Jackson, Alan Gardner (Short Wave Magazine), P.W. Publishing, Mike Devereaux (Nevada Communications), Amanda Taylor (Tandy), Chris Foster (Sandpiper Aerials), S.M.C. Limited, Icom (UK), Sony (UK), Lowe Electronics, Revco Electronics and the many readers who wrote to me with suggestions, information and observations on equipment.

Introduction 1

Welcome to the revised edition of *Scanners* which I hope will not only answer the many questions that new scanner owners ask but will also provide a valuable reference source. If you bought the original issue of the book then I hope you enjoy this new edition with its updated information and very much expanded section on frequency allocations. Naturally, some sections of the book have not been altered; it would be pointless to change the text for the sake of it.

Caution

The aim of this book is to provide a basic understanding of the use of scanning receivers and VHF/UHF communications. Contrary to popular belief this type of equipment is *not* solely purchased by people who have no legitimate right to listen in to certain kinds of radio traffic and who wish to illegally snoop on other people's messages. Many people from amateurs to commercial and professional users buy this type of equipment for perfectly legitimate reasons. However, such people may still not fully understand how to use the scanner to its best ability. This book is aimed at all scanner users who want a better understanding of how their equipment works. In order to achieve that aim it has been necessary to include a wide range of information, some of which might be considered sensitive. I must stress that although certain bands and frequency allocations are shown, the book should *not* be interpreted as an invitation to listen-in — unless the appropriate licence or authority is held.

To sum up: *The responsibility lies with the equipment owner to satisfy himself that he has a legal right to listen-in to any radio transmission.* All information published here has been published before at some time, much of it by the Government. However its publication here must not be interpreted as some kind of right to listen-in. The unlicensed user will find the following information useful.

The legal position

The very existence of scanning receivers has been shrouded with some controversy and, indeed, some countries are planning to ban their sale except to professional or licensed users. Governments have become increasingly worried because use of a scanner clearly enables anyone to tune into transmissions of possibly sensitive natures (police and military being typical examples).

But what is the law? It varies from country to country and clearly it is beyond the scope of this book to provide a global definition. In the USA legislation even varies from state to state. It may be quite legal to listen in to police transmissions in one state but an offence to do so in the next. Some states allow listening-in on a portable or base station but not in a moving vehicle.

What about Britain? In England, Scotland, Wales, Northern Ireland, the Isle of Man and the Channel Islands the relevant law is the Wireless Telegraphy Act and its various amendments. Put simply, the Act says that members of the public are entitled to listen to only two kinds of broadcast; licensed broadcast stations (ie, BBC, Local Radio or foreign equivalents, etc) or licensed radio amateurs. In this respect, it is an offence to listen-in to any other broadcasts.

There is a myth that says you can listen-in to anything as long as you do not act on information received or pass on to someone else the contents of any transmission heard. But be warned that this is not so and there have been instances where courts have fined people who have been caught listening-in to police transmissions.

As for scanner users in other countries they are well advised to get advice on their local legal position.

Licences

Having warned about the possible consequences of tuning in to transmissions other than amateur or broadcast it should be stated that licences *are* available to listen-in to, and indeed transmit on, certain frequencies. The most notable are amateur, marine, aviation and Citizens band (CB) licences but it should be stressed that with the exception of CB, licences are only issued to people who have passed relevant examinations. In the case of marine and aircraft these examinations are based on operation and radio procedure rather than technical knowledge. In the case of the amateur licence, however, a basic knowledge of electronics is also required. Information on these licences is available from the following bodies:

Any Post Office (CB).
Any CAA Approved Flying School.
Department of Trade and Industry (Marine).
Radio Society of Great Britain (Amateur).

Changes and trends

I said in the Introduction to the first edition of this book that we were likely to see several trends develop in both scanner technology and the use of VHF/UHF communications generally. It's surprising how in just four years so much has changed. Although voice scrambling has not taken off to any large degree it's interesting to note that the new portable telephone system known as 'Telepoint' or CT2 is using digitised speech which cannot be picked up by an ordinary receiver. As for frequency allocations, since the first edition was published we have seen considerable expansion of use of the old Band III television channels.

Equipment has moved fairly much along the lines I predicted with new highly sophisticated models from Icom and AOR. One surprise newcomer has been Kenwood with their unusual car radio cum scanner. One thing that has become apparent is that the scanner craze has made many people realise that there is also a lot of interesting listening to be done on the lower HF or Short Wave bands as well and so now we have seen the introduction of scanners which tune from the Long Waves right up through to the UHF bands.

Perhaps the non-event of the last four years has been the use of scanners under computer control. I am now convinced that this is largely due to the problems of spurious emissions from computers made for the British market. Although at least four available scanners can be brought under computer control, the scanner will lock-up on the many signals generated within the unscreened computer. Sadly and for reasons that are not at all clear, the British government have lagged well behind most of the world in introducing standards to cut down radiation from microprocessor controlled equipment (I even get substantial problems from equipment operated in premises some distance from my own home). If you have the technical know-how to start screening equipment and leads then I still maintain that this type of operation opens up a whole new world of scanning (the companion book *Scanners 2* offers practical advice on solving the interference problems).

Finally, as predicted, hand portables have now started to offer wider coverage, particularly sets from Black Jaguar, AOR, Tandy and the re-born Bearcat Company (now Uniden-Bearcat). I personally think they are still missing out and that there is an enormous market waiting for a proper no-gaps coverage, AM/FM programmable handset. Imagine an AOR2001 or Realistic PRO-2004 in a portable package and you have the picture. I cannot believe that it is technically impossible — a look inside an AOR will reveal a lot of fresh air despite its small size.

Predictions for the next four years? I have a sneaking suspicion that some up-market domestic radio receivers might start to offer limited scanning of some of the more popular communication bands such as air and marine. Sony have led a move in that direction and who knows who may follow.

Peter Rouse
Guernsey 1989

A basic understanding of 2 radio

One question frequently asked by first time scanner buyers is 'how far away from stations can I be in order to still pick up the signals?'. This is a bit like asking 'how long is a piece of string?'. Radio signals are transmitted in different ways and, at the frequencies covered by most scanners, the signals are greatly affected by a number of factors including;

The frequency used.
The time of year.
The aerial used.
The location of the scanner.
The location of the transmitting station.
The weather.

To understand why these factors affect range you need to have a basic understanding of the way radio signals travel. If you are prepared to try and understand the basics in simple layman's terms then you will go a long way to getting the best out of your equipment. But, if not, then skip this chapter.

Receivers and transmitters

Before we go any further we must understand in simple terms just what receivers and transmitters are. The transmitter is a device which generates an electromagnetic signal that will radiate from an aerial. The power, that is, strength of the signal as it is transmitted is measured in watts. For instance, a CB radio transmitter may have a power of about four watts, but a medium wave broadcast transmitter power might be as much as 1 million watts — better known as a megawatt. The allowable transmitter power used in any application is normally stipulated in Government regulations. Obviously, a broadcast transmitter has to send its signals long distances in order to reach the large number of people that make up the station's audience, so it will need to be of high power. On the other hand, a taxi firm operating in one town will only need to contact cabs over only a few miles and so the required power level is much lower. Normally, but there are exceptions, the transmitter sends out what is called a radio frequency 'carrier wave' and the speech, music or other information to be transmitted is superimposed on this wave. There are several 'modes' of doing this, discussed later in the chapter.

The receiver, in this case the scanner, needs an aerial to 'gather up' the radio frequency transmitted signal. The aerial is not selective enough to gather up the required signal alone, and a number of other signals that happen to be on the air at the same time are presented to the receiver. These signals are first 'amplified', that is, boosted, after which they enter a stage within the receiver where the wanted signal is isolated from the rest. This is further amplified before going through what is called a 'detector' or 'demodulator' which converts the radio frequency signal back into the speech, music or other information originally super-imposed on the carrier wave.

Most of the transmissions you hear on a scanner will be from equipment called 'transceivers' — the term is an abridged name for transmitter/receiver. That is because most scanners cover the radio bands allocated to communications therefore the stations you hear will be talking back and forth to each other and so will need to transmit *and* receive.

A scanner is a very sophisticated type of receiver. Instead of just being tuned to one frequency at a time, it has special circuits which allow a whole range of frequencies to be programmed in by the user. The scanner then steps through all these frequencies (usually referred to as channels), stopping when it finds a transmission. Once the transmission ends the scanner carries on through the channels to find the next one with a transmission taking place.

Frequency/wavelength spectrum

One of the first topics that causes confusion among newcomers to radio is that of the frequency spectrum and the corresponding relationship between frequency and wavelength. Having established that we are going to transmit a signal we have to transmit it at a particular frequency. At the receiving end, as you tune across the dial of a normal radio, you will find a whole range of transmissions, but each one is at a different point on the dial, that is, each has a different frequency. You are tuning through part of what is called the 'frequency spectrum'. In practical terms try and imagine a radio which does not have separate switched bands for, say, medium and long wave, but instead has a great big long tuning dial. Let's say that the left hand side is the lowest frequency for transmitting, corresponding to 15 kilohertz. That means that the received transmission at this point will 'resonate' or vibrate at 15 thousand cycles per second (kilo, in radio and electronics terms, simply means thousand: hertz means cycles per second). As we tune from left to right the received frequency becomes greater and we pass through those frequencies allocated for long wave broadcasting. When we get to about 550kHz (kHz is the abbreviation for kilohertz) we come to the medium wave broadcast band which carries on up to 1600kHz. However, at this point we drop the term kilohertz because 1600 kilohertz equals 1.6 megahertz (mega — meaning million). We carry on tuning upwards, passing through what is called medium frequency (MF for short) and we now come into what in the past has been referred to as short wave but is now known as high frequency (HF). We can continue tuning until we get even higher in frequency to 30 MHz (MHz is the abbreviation for megahertz). Above this we are in what is called very high frequency (VHF). We can carry on much further and will come next to ultra high frequency (UHF), then on to super high frequency (SHF) and extremely high frequency (EHF): more commonly called 'microwaves'.

Notice that all the time we have been talking about frequency we have related it to waves and wavelengths. That is because at any point on the dial we can define the transmission as a frequency *or* as a wavelength – any given frequency has a corresponding wavelength, and vice versa.

Table 2.1 relates the various frequency divisions together with the corresponding ranges. Dividing the radio frequency spectrum up in this

Table 2.1 Radio frequency spectrum, each division as a frequency range

Frequency division	*Frequency range*
Very low frequency (VLF)	3-30 kHz
Low frequency (LF)	30-300 kHz
Medium frequency (MF)	300-3000 kHz
High frequency (HF)	3-30 MHz
Very high frequency (VHF)	30-300 MHz
Ultra high frequency (UHF)	300-3000 MHz
Super high frequency (SHF)	3-30 GHz
Extremely high frequency (EHF)	30-300 GHz
No designation	300-3000 GHz

k = kilo = x1,000.
M = mega = x1,000,000.
G = giga = x1,000,000,000

way is simply a matter of convenience — most radio transmitters and receivers aren't capable of tuning over the whole spectrum in one go, as our imaginary radio can, and switched divisions are required. The divisions given in Table 2.1 are those generally accepted worldwide.

From now on this book will be dealing mainly with the VHF and UHF division bands and so for the most part we will be talking about megahertz, although there will be reference to kilohertz when we discuss channel spacing and bandwidth.

So where do scanners fit in to all of this? Some, like the synthesised types, cover anywhere between 26 MHz at the top end of HF and, in the case of Icom, 2000MHz (2GHz) at UHF. There are also scanners which cover the HF bands, but they do not really cover the categories of communications dealt with by this book.

Distances

Now back to the question of distances we asked at the start of the chapter. In order to answer that question we need to look at what is called 'propagation', which is the way radio signals actually travel. There are three main ways a signal gets from one point to another.

As a **groundwave**. The signal travels virtually in a straight line between the two points.
As a **skywave**. The signal leaves one point, travels skywards and bounces off part of the ionosphere, back to earth.
Via **tropospherical ducting**. The signal travels above ground, through a conductive layer caused by the junction of warm and cold air currents.

Ground wave (Figure 2.1)
The ground wave is the main means of propagation for signals above 30MHz. However, at frequencies slightly above and below 30MHz, other conditions prevail at times but we will look at those in a moment

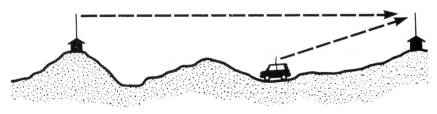

Figure 2.1 Ground wave. Typically 'line of sight' at VHF and UHF.

For VHF and UHF communications it is generally fair to say that the ground wave transmission distance is limited to what is called 'line of sight'. That means that if there were no obstructions such as buildings or high ground around us the signal would only travel as far as we can see on a clear day, in other words to the horizon. In practical terms this means that communication between two stations on the ground is usually limited at the most to around 30 miles. Obviously if the transmitting station is on very high ground this range will increase and if we are flying at thousands of feet in an aircraft the range increases even further. Other factors which effect this range are such things as transmitter power; obviously the more powerful the transmitter the further the range, although there does come a point where even masses of increase in transmitter power will make little difference to the range of the signal.

Skywave (Figure 2.2)

As its name suggests, the skywave is that part of the signal from the transmitting aerial that travels upwards. Also known as ionospheric propagation, it is the main means of propagation of frequencies below 30MHz. What happens is that the signal travels up to the ionosphere where it bounces back off one of the several layers of ionised gas. Normally the ionisation is not dense enough to bounce back the much smaller VHF and UHF radio waves. However it will bounce back the bigger waves encountered in the HF bands.

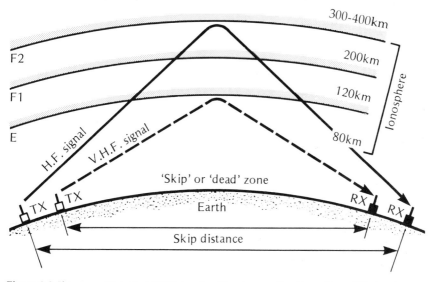

Figure 2.2 Sky wave. Note that VHF signals will not normally skip as far as HF signals.

We can draw an analogy here which will illustrate how this effect occurs: imagine the ionosphere as a screen of chicken mesh. If we gather a handful of different sized stones and think of the bigger stones as representing the lower HF frequencies while the smaller stones are the higher VHF/UHF frequencies; then throw our stones at the chicken mesh, the bigger stones bounce back at us but the smaller ones pass right through the mesh. In simple terms that is roughly what happens to our radio waves.

There are several different layers in the ionosphere which affect the skywave. They are the E, F1 and F2 layers. The F2 layer is the one largely responsible for bouncing back HF signals and at certain times (such as during the winter months and at night) it tends to combine with the F1 layer. The more densely ionised the gases are, the more they are capable of bouncing back signals at higher frequencies. The degree of ionisation depends on radiation from the sun and so during daylight hours and the summer months the ionisation increases and higher frequencies start bouncing back to earth. Put simply, the more ionisation, the higher in frequency the reflection occurs.

This phenomenon is also subject to quite spectacular peaks. There is an 11 year cycle in which solar flares on the sun's surface cause higher than usual radiation. In the lead up to this peak and after it, ionisation is so intense that it is not unusual for low powered signals to travel right round the world. This latter effect is called 'multi-hop' and here the signal hits the ionosphere, bounces back to earth, bounces back up again and so forth. The last peak of the cycle was in 1980.

The area on the ground between the signal going up and coming back down again is known as the 'skip zone' or dead zone'. The distance a reflected signal travels between two points on the ground is called the 'skip distance'.

The skywave effect we have talked about so far is generally limited to frequencies below 50MHz. Above that frequency, however, a similar effect takes place due to the E layer which reflects VHF signals. The phenomenon usually happens only during the summer months, when sudden heavy ionisation lasting but a very short period of time — just a few hours in some cases — occurs. Hence, the effect is known as 'sporadic-E'. It can affect frequencies from the upper end of HF to as high as 150MHz in the VHF bands. Typical ranges under these conditions may be distances of 800 miles or more at VHF.

Above 150MHz it becomes rarer for signals to be affected by any kind of reflection from the ionosphere.

Tropospherical ducting (Figure 2.3)
Tropospherical duting is responsible for most of the freak long-distance reception that the scanner user will encounter.

The effect takes place at around 2000 meters above the ground, and occurs mostly during the summer when, under the right weather conditions, a cold air stream meets a warm air stream forming a sort of 'pipe' which ducts the signal along for great distances. Tropospherical ducting (so called because the 'pipe' is formed in the layer known as the

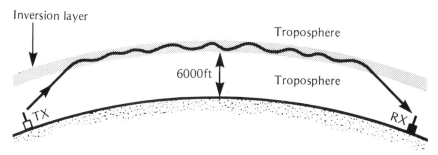

Figure 2.3 Tropospherical ducting 'Tropo'.

troposphere) is most common at VHF and UHF frequencies, but it can extend to microwaves at times.

Ranges under these conditions vary enormously but, as an example, it is quite common to work distances of several hundred miles or more in the 2 metre amateur band.

Any effect, such as these three, which occurs to increase the range of the signals is often referred to as a 'lift' or 'lift conditions'.

Modes of modulation (Figure 2.4)

The simplest of radio signals consist of nothing more than a carrier wave switched on and off. If the switching is spaced to produce dots and dashes we have morse code, or CW as it is often called. The average

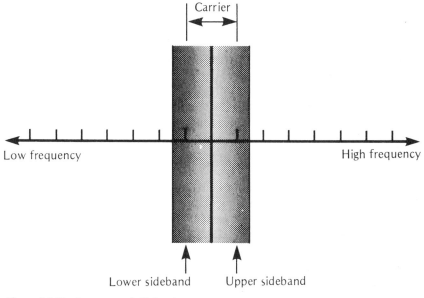

Figure 2.4 Carrier wave and sidebands.

scanner user is unlikely to be interested in morse code and, indeed, the majority of scanners are not capable of reproducing it anyway.

What is of more interest is a carrier wave that has an audio signal such as speech superimposed on it. There are several ways of superimposing an audio signal on a radio carrier wave signal and one method even does away with the carrier wave altogether.

Amplitude modulation (AM)

In amplitude modulation the audio signal is used to control the amplitude of the carrier. If we display this graphically on an oscilloscope we see that, in fact, the carrier is broken up into what are known as 'envelopes' (see Figure 2.5). The envelopes change in sympathy with the

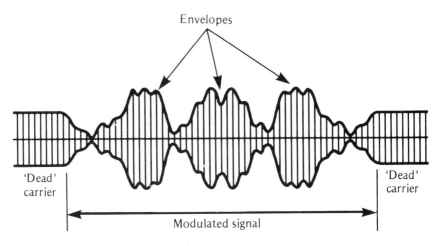

Figure 2.5 Amplitude modulation.

audio signal. At the receiving end the simple circuit that converts the amplitude modulated carrier back into an audio signal is called a 'detector'. Unfortunately its simplicity can cause problems for other electronic equipment sited near the transmitter. One problem is the breakthrough of signals into equipment such as record players, baby alarms, intercoms, etc, containing audio amplifiers. The solid state devices in these amplifiers can, given a strong enough signal, act as detectors which reproduce the transmitted signal.

AM as a mode is now largely being superseded by FM which has several advantages, one of which is that it does not cause the same level of breakthrough. AM is still in use, though, on some private mobile radio bands, some European CB channels and the international aircraft band.

Frequency modulation (FM)

This works on an entirely different concept, illustrated in Figure 2.6. Here the *frequency* of the carrier is shifted rapidly up and down in sympathy with the audio signal. The difference in frequency between the lowest and highest points is called the 'deviation'. In a broadcast FM transmitter the deviation may be as much as 150kHz but, in the case of a transceiver which a scanner tunes into, deviation is kept quite low to limit its use of the radio spectrum (typically 5kHz).

The smaller the deviation, the smaller is the transmitted radio signal 'bandwidth', ie, the amount of frequency spectrum taken up by the radio signal. A small, or narrow bandwidth means that the signal will take up less space in a given band and for communication bands this means we are able to slot more channels into a given band. The result obviously is that we can get more users on the air in a given band space.

At the receiving end, the method of converting the signal back into audio is far more complex than with AM. The circuit that does the

Constant amplitude

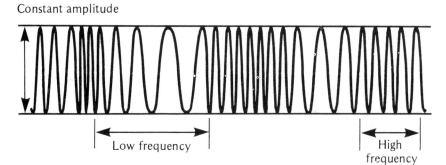

Low frequency

High frequency

Figure 2.6(a) Frequency modulation

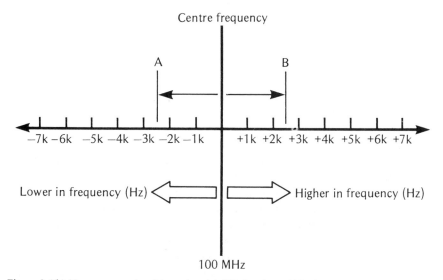

Figure 2.6(b) How a narrowband (speech only) FM signal would look if we could graphically show it on a radio dial. The lowest frequency (bass) sounds would shift the frequency towards 'A' whilst the highest sounds (treble) would shift towards 'B'.

conversion is known as a 'demodulator' or 'discriminator'. It is the complexity of this conversion process that makes the mode less likely to be demodulated by circuitry in audio equipment of the type that AM can interfere with.

FM is now widely used in communications. It will be found on most land mobile allocations and is the only mode used on the marine VHF band.

An AM detector *can* be used to resolve an FM signal just as an FM detector *can* resolve an AM signal. However, in both instances the received audio will be noisy, weak and probably distorted. Wherever possible the correct demodulator/detector should be used. It is possible to get passable reception of an FM signal from an AM detector by slightly off-tuning. The receiver is then partly tuned into the side-band and this method of operation is known as 'slope detection'.

Single sideband (SSB)

Refer back to Figure 2.4 and you will see that we still have not talked about the two sidebands. Each sideband actually contains all the information relating to the transmitted audio signal, so in theory it is possible to transmit the signal without a carrier at all. Nevertheless, the audio signal is initially superimposed onto the carrier in a similar way to AM transmission.

However, special filters in the transmitter remove the carrier wave and one of the sidebands. Most SSB transmitters have a switch that allows either the upper or lower sideband to be removed. With only a single sideband to be transmitted it is apparent that even less bandspace than either AM or FM is required so a greater number of channels may be crammed into a given band.

SSB may seem the ideal solution to the crowded airwaves but unfortunately it has some drawbacks — particularly for mobile operation. At the receiving end we have to re-insert the missing carrier wave before we can carry out the detection process. The carrier wave we put back in is generated by a beat frequency oscillator (BFO) which has to be tuned precisely to match the frequency of the incoming signal . . . even the slightest off-tuning can make the detected audio signal distorted, sounding very much like someone imitating Donald Duck. Obviously, a mobile operator cannot drive and re-tune at the same time. A further problem exists because the circuits in the transmitter and receiver are far more complex and AM or FM equivalents, so SSB equipment is far more costly

The greatest users of SSB on the VHF/UHF bands are amateurs and in Chapter 7 you will find bandplans for the amateur service which show where most SSB operation takes place. However, there are only two scanners available in the UK that can properly receive SSB transmissions. These are the Yaesu and Icom.

For the practically adept, a suitable circuit to modify the SX-200 is available in kit form from Cirkit (address at back of book). Having fitted one of these to my own SX-200 I can see no reason why it should not be adapted to other sets although a suitable injection point for the BFO signal is required.

The fine tuning needed for SSB is carried out in one of two ways. On better equipment, the switch marked USB (upper sideband) or LSB (lower sideband) will switch the BFO to the appropriate frequency. Fine tuning of the receiver is then carried out until clear speech is heard.

The second method, found on cheaper equipment, is a bit cruder. First, the receiver is tuned roughly to the incoming signal; second, the BFO frequency is tuned to get clear speech. The disadvantage with this method is that it is often necessary to jiggle around between the receiver's tuning the BFO setting to get it right.

Channelising (Figure 2.7)

Channelising is often something of a mystery to the newcomer to radio and yet it is quite simple to understand.

We can take part of the radio spectrum and divide it up into blocks. If, for instance, we were to take that segment of the spectrum from 150 to 150.90MHz we could divide it up into 10 'spot frequencies' starting with 150.00MHz, then 150.10MHz, then 150.20MHz and so forth until we

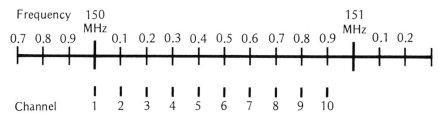

Figure 2.7 Channelising. Any section of the radio spectrum can be divided up and each spot frequency given a channel number.

reach 150.90MHz. We now have 10 spot frequencies, with separations of 100KHz, which may be allocated as radio transmission channels and could be numbered, in this case, from 1 to 10. We can do this to any part of the radio spectrum although, in practice, it does not always follow that the channels are numbered in the sequence they appear in the spectrum. Take a look at the Marine bands in Chapter 7 and you will see a typical example of this.

A large proportion of the VHF/UHF spectrum is split up into channels. In some bands, they are referred to by a channel number but in other bands by the actual frequency that the channel is on. Again, you will see in Chapter 7 that the entire marine band is referred to by channel numbers. However, although the aircraft band is also divided up into channels, they are always referred to by frequency.

The separation between channels quite naturally is referred to as 'channel separation'. This separation tends to vary a bit between the different bands simply because over the years some separations have been reduced to fit more channels into a given band. Typical these days though, is 12.5kHz separation at VHF and 25kHZ separation at UHF. Remember what we said earlier about limiting the deviation to around 5kHZ at VHF. If we deduct that from the 12.5kHz separation we get 7.5kHz. Divide that by two to get 3.75kHz and that is the amount of spare space either side of the transmitted signal. This space, sometimes called a 'guard band', ensures that the signal does not splash over into the next channel causing interference to other operators.

As a general rule, any band where the operator is permitted to use a range of frequencies will be split up into numbered channels. It is easier and quicker for, say, CB or marine operators, to say to each other 'change to channel 10' than it is to start rattling off an actual frequency — allowing they could remember what the centre frequency of a particular channel is.

On the other hand, private mobile radio operators who work solely on their own allocated channel will have it allocated as a frequency. So, the PMR bands *are* split up into channels, however, they are not numbered and are referred to by frequency.

Types of transmission

The VHF/UHF bands are used for a variety of transmissions and these fall into four broad categories; audio, morse, television and data (teletype, fax, etc). These categories must not be confused with modulation modes. Most of the following transmission types can be transmitted in any mode.

Audio
This, of course, takes the form of simple speech or, in the case of broadcasts, it may be music. Indeed any sounds that the human ear can interpret may be transmitted.

Morse
One of the simplest forms of communications, morse consists of nothing more than a series od dots and dashes. The duration of the switching on and off of a carrier wave makes up the dots and dashes which can be interpreted by a skilled operator into letters, numbers and punctuation.

Although there *are* morse transmissions at VHF/UHF, few scanners are able to receive them. The transmitted signal contains no tone of any kind and, in order to get the familiar 'beep', the scanner must be fitted with a beat frequency oscillator. Without this, morse will simply sound like a series of soft rhythmic clicks.

Television

This can take two forms. The most familiar type is normal broadcast television which is known as 'broadband/fast scan'. The Yaesu-Musen, Kenwood and Icom scanners have the circuitry (as an optional extra) to demodulate these signals. The Icom can be fitted with an adaptor for the British PAL system but the Yaesu and Kenwood demodulators only work with the NTSC system used in North America.

Amateurs also use this type of transmission to send not only black and white but also colour pictures between themselves. Special equipment is needed for this and operation is limited to the UHF bands.

Another form of television used by amateurs is called 'slow scan television'; SSTV for short. This is a method of sending drawings and still photographs, taking several seconds to transmit a single frame, which is built up slowly, line by line. Scanner owners who are interested in these transmissions will be interested to know that if they also own one of the popular home micro-computers, then using a simple adaptor and appropriate software it is possible to reproduce these pictures on a normal television set. Details of adaptors and software are given in Chapter 6.

If, when scanning amateur bands, you hear what sounds like a period of buzzing noises that rise and fall in pitch with a regular blip at the end of each burst, then it is probably SSTV.

Facsimile

This again is a method of sending drawings or still pictures over the air. Popularly called 'fax', it works on virtually identical principles to SSTV. Scanner users can easily pick-up fax transmissions from the weather satellites and, as with SSTV, it is possible to convert these signals (which usually sound like a series of bleeps or tones) with the help of a home computer. Again Chapter 6 gives more details.

RTTY

RTTY (an acronym for radio teletype) is, simply, a teleprinter used to send messages by radio rather than by telephone line. RTTY is used at VHF/UHF by amateurs and, again, it is a means of communication that can be decoded by a home computer. However, to receive these transmissions you will need to have a BFO circuit on the receiver (see the morse code section above). The received signals sound like speeded up morse code although they do actually consist of two alternating tones.

ASCII

ASCII (the American Standard Code for Information Interchange) is the 'language' that computers use to store and send programs or data, and it is occasionally transmitted, particularly by amateurs when they want to swap computer programs, over the air. Although many scanners are capable of receiving such transmissions, which sound exactly like a computer program cassette played back through a loudspeaker, any transmissions received will only be of use if the scanner owner owns a compatible computer. However, such transmissions are usually preceded by normal voice communications between the amateurs concerned and so some idea will be gained of what the program is, which computer it is for and when they are going to start sending. Should the scanner owner be able to make use of the program then it is simply a matter of recording it off air via the scanner's record or earphone socket.

Odd sounds

Occasionally odd signals may be heard which do not fit into any of the above categories. These can be anything from navigation beacons to telemetry signals sending data.

Simplex/Duplex operation

There is often misunderstanding over the expressions 'simplex' and 'duplex', together with their derivatives, and the situation is not helped by the fact that different groups of communications users have different interpretations. Generally, the terms refer to whether the communication is one-way at a time, or two-way. For the purposes of this book the following definitions are assumed.

Simplex

This is the easiest operation to understand. For instance you will hear typical simplex transmissions on the civilian aircraft band. You can hear both sides of a conversation on one frequency. So we know that station A transmits on a particular frequency, while station B listens. Then station B transmits on the same frequency while station A listens. In other words only one station transmits at any one time, and only one frequency is used, so one station must wait for the other to finish transmission, before transmitting itself.

Split or dual frequency simplex (Figure 2.8)

In some sections of the VHF/UHF spectrum, you may well pick up transmissions where you can only hear one side of a conversation, even though the station you cannot hear may be in range. There are several types of this kind of communications which use two frequencies instead

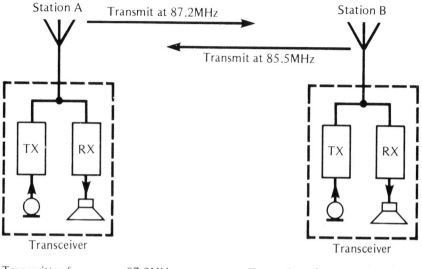

Transmitter frequency: 87.2MHz
Receiver frequency: 85.5MHz

Transmitter frequency: 85.5MHz
Receiver frequency: 87.2MHz

Figure 2.8 Split frequency simplex.

of one and the example we consider here is known as 'split frequency simplex'. In this, station A transmits on, say, 85.5MHz. But when station B transmits, a different frequency, say, 87.2MHz, is used. Each station still must wait its turn to transmit. When picking up these kinds of transmission the scanner owner has to programme both frequencies into his scanner in order to hear both sides of the conversation.

It may well seem that it is a waste of spectrum space to use two frequencies for communications when ordinary simplex could have been used to achieve the same end result. However, split frequency simplex has some advantages for some communicators, the greatest of which is that it allows the use of what are known as 'repeaters' (see Figure 2.9). Let us assume that the repeater and its aerials (one for receive the other for transmit) are on good high ground. Portable set A transmits and is picked up by the base station receiver which feeds the signal to the base station transmitter and re-broadcasts it. Portable set B, which is well out of normal working distance from portable A is able to pick up the signals easily. And of course the system will work in reverse allowing B to talk back to A.

Repeaters, as used by amateurs, operate like this all the time. They have computer controlled circuitry to switch the transmitter on when a signal is received and shut down again when no one is using it. Some repeaters activate automatically on any signal containing speech others require a short burst of tone from the incoming signal to switch on. Repeaters are not supposed to be used for long conversations and so

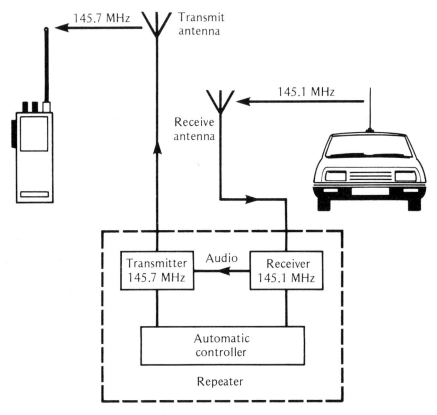

Figure 2.9 Repeater. Automatic turn-on and turn-off. In the case of 'talkthrough' the switching controller is operated manually.

have a built-in timer which switches the transmitter off after a pre-determined time.

Another advantage of split frequency simplex is that it allows 'talkthrough'. Talkthrough is often used by such bodies as the police for the odd occasion that two mobile units may need to liaise with each other. In this case the talkthrough is actually switched over manually at the base station or control centre.

Although these are instances of split frequency working, the scanner needs only be tuned to the output of the repeater to be able to hear both sides of the conversation

Duplex

Duplex operation is most easily understood with reference to the telephone, where two-way communications can take place simultaneously, that is, both users can speak and listen at the same time. A dual frequency method of working as described in split frequency simplex is used, but here the stations have their transmitters and receivers both on at the same time. It means that a normal telephone-type conversation can take place and indeed duplex operation is mostly used to put normal telephone calls, over the air, to ships, cars and in the case of the USA, aircraft.

Half duplex

This works in a similar way to duplex operation but is not quite so sophisticated, even though it does allow a radio system to be connected to the normal telephone system. The base station operates in much the same way as in duplex in that the transmitter and receiver will both be on at the same time. However, the mobile unit is only able to transmit *or* receive at any one time. In some instances, the operator needs to key the microphone but in other cases a circuit called a 'vox', short for voice operated switch, will automatically switch to transmit every time the mobile operator speaks.

Scanner users are most likely to encounter half duplex operation on the marine bands and mobile telephone frequencies. On the marine bands it is used for a system known as 'link calls', where communications between ship and shore allow telephone calls to be either originated or received on the vessel. Similarly the system is used extensively for mobile telephones in cars on networks available in some larger cities.

Both duplex and half duplex operations present some problems for the scanner owner because, as two frequencies are being used simultaneously, it is only possible to pick up one side of the conversation.

3 The hardware

Scanners come in a variety of shapes, sizes and types. They also vary very much in quality and performance. As a general rule, though, they are more sophisticated and built to a higher standard than most portable radios used for broadcast reception. They are designed to cover a number of frequencies so that they may be used to monitor several transmissions. This, of course, is because communications signals, unlike broadcasts, are not transmitted constantly and are only transmitted when there are messages.

In order to fully cover the different types of scanner we have to divide them into two distinct types; 'crystal controlled' and synthesised. In the case of crystal controlled scanners it is necessary to plug into the circuit small quartz crystals which oscillate at the frequency you want to receive. Once you have installed such a crystal you are stuck with that frequency — other crystals are needed for different frequencies.

Synthesised scanners, on the other hand, don't need such crystals. They incorporate a sophisticated circuit, which is controlled by a small computer, to generate the frequencies required. Any change in frequency is merely programmed in, usually through a calculator-style keyboard on the front panel.

As a rule, crystal controlled scanners are much cheaper than synthesised ones but bear in mind that crystals are expensive. In the case of, say, a ten channel air band scanner, the ten crystals might cost as much as the scanner itself.

Crystal controlled scanners

The photo on page 145 shows a typical crystal controlled scanner. These were the first scanners ever to appear and, despite their main disadvantage of crystal changing requirements, are still popular. They are normally only capable of covering a small number of channels: a minimum of about four and a maximum of about 16. Also, these channels must be fairly close together in frequency. However, there is an exception in some of the models sold by the Tandy Corporation, which are capable of tuning over two given bands, with a certain number of channels allocated to each of those bands.

The main advantage of crystal controlled scanners is that they can be made quite small — there are examples of units covering as many as ten channels while still being little bigger than the size of a cigarette packet.

Chapter 4 gives details on how to change the crystals in these scanners.

Synthesised scanners

The photo on page 184 shows a typical synthesised scanner. Synthesised scanners sub-divide into two categories. The first works in a similar way to the crystal controlled types but the difference is that a synthesiser is used for tuning instead. Such scanners allow you to programme in a number of channels but do not allow instant access from front panel controls to dial in new channels. So like crystal controlled scanners, although no expensive crystals are involved, the scanner is limited to stepping through pre-set channels.

A variation on this method is 'frequency-stepping' via buttons on the front panel. This type of programming is found on such sets as the 'Fairmate'. Here there are several buttons, one steps in units of 10MHz, the next in 1MHz, then 100KHz, and so on. The procedure is to keep pressing the buttons until the required digits appear on the digital frequency readout. The method is a bit like the system used to set digital timers and clocks on such things as videorecorders. This type of programming presents no problems where only a selection of pre-set channels are ever monitored. However, it is a very slow method of programming and not suited to rapid entry of a new frequency. Sets with calculator-type input keyboards are much quicker.

The second kind of synthesised scanner offers the same programmed-channel scan facility as the previous type of synthesised scanner but can also 'search' for signals by continuously and automatically tuning through the bands. For instance, you can programme the scanner to search from, say, 100MHz to 200MHz, whereupon it will start at the lowest frequency and slowly tune upwards to the highest. If it finds any transmissions it will lock onto them but, if not, it will start again at the bottom and again work through the selected band. The big advantage this offers is that it enables the user to find all sorts of transmissions previously unheard. Once found, a communication channel frequency may be programmed into the scanner's memory, for use another time.

Another big advantage with this facility is that it's possible to locate a particular transmission when only an approximate frequency is known.

For instance if you knew a certain station occasionally transmitted at about 145.5MHz you can set the scanner to search rapidly over and over again between 145 and 146MHz until the station starts to transmit.

In addition to searching you can of course use these sets for true scanning. That is getting the equipment to run through a series of channels that you have programmed with the frequencies you want to listen in to. Most current sets have memories for 16 or more channels which hold the channel frequencies even when the set is switched off. A couple of small cells or a special capacitor provide power requirements for the memory circuit. Normally the batteries will last a year or more but users should always remember to write down the frequencies because when the batteries require replacement all channels will require consequent re-programming. In the case of scanners such as the AOR, a small capacitor holds enough charge to keep the memory active. Although the capacitor is re-charged every time the set is used it is only good for about a fortnight between charges.

Frequency coverage

Scanners vary enormously in the range of frequencies that they cover. More modern and expensive ones like the AOR2002, SX-400, Yaesu-Musen and Icom cover a very wide range of frequencies from VHF through to UHF. Other sets, though, such as most of the Bearcats and Radio-Shack (Tandy) models and the SX-200 leave out certain frequency bands and so there are gaps in their coverage. At times this can be a nuisance because it means you cannot tune-in to certain interesting bands. The reason some scanners skip certain bands is because it is either cheaper for them to be made that way or they are not really designed for the European markets. Most scanners are made in Japan and are designed for the American market. In the USA some bands are allocated for entirely different kinds of transmissions to those used in Europe. As an example, owners of the SX-200 have often been frustrated that the set does not cover the section of the VHF band from 88 to 108MHz. In America this band is used exclusively for VHF broadcasting which is of little interest to scanner users, but in Britain it is presently used for such things as private mobile radio and emergency service transmissions, too.

When choosing a scanner it is a good idea to have a list of the frequencies you wish to cover before deciding on the model you will buy. It is not unknown for salesmen, often through sheer ignorance, to completely misinform a potential customer on what transmissions a particular type of scanner will pick up. Details of who transmits on what frequencies are covered in Chapter 7.

Strange switches and knobs

For the newcomer to scanning, the front panel of his equipment can present a bewildering array of control knobs and switches often labelled with unfamiliar names (see Photo 3(a)). Unlike the elaborate knobs and switches found on some modern hi-fi equipment these controls are not just for show. The wide range of conditions found on communications frequencies means the scanner owner must be able to select various options for such things as mode, channel spacing, bandwidth, etc.

Photograph 3(a) A typical modern scanner control panel. Note that several of the push-buttons double up for more than one use such as mode or step rate as well as a digit for frequency.

Usually, the more expensive the scanner the more control the owner has over the way it operates. There follows descriptions of most controls found on modern scanners.

Squelch or mute
A 'squelch' control, occasionally called 'mute', can be found on most types of VHF and UHF equipment used in communications. It is a form of electronic switch which cuts off the audio signal when the radio is not receiving anything. The reason for this is quite simple: if the scanner is tuned to a channel with no transmission in it and the audio was not switched off, the listener would have to put up with the constant roaring hiss of amplifying circuits, the crackle of static and noise from a variety

of sources of interference. In scanning, the control takes on another important role because the circuit that actually steps through the pre-programmed channels is activated by the squelch. So when there is no received signal the squelch tells the scanner to keep hunting until it finds a channel where there is someone transmitting. Once found the squelch 'opens' and that causes the scanning circuit to stop and so lock on to that active channel.

There are three main types of squelch found on scanners. Some sets will only include one type whereas more elaborate equipment will allow the operator to select the kind of squelch he wishes to use.

Carrier squelch

This is the simplest (in electrical terms) kind of squelch and is best situated to reception of AM signals. It works by detecting the presence of a carrier wave and simply shuts the audio on and off. The main disadvantage of this type of squelch is that it will activate on some types of interference such as car ignition noise and static.

Deviation muting

Despite the term muting, it is still squelch and in this instance is only suitable for FM reception. However, it is far more effective than carrier squelch when it comes to ignoring the types of interference mentioned above. This type of squelch is often encountered as the sole means of muting on some crystal controlled scanners such as the pocket-sized ones available for the amateur 2 metre and marine bands. This type of squelch does not respond to varying signal strength but instead detects the actual deviation (see Chapter 2) of the FM signal.

Voice squelch

Also known as 'AF scan', voice squelch is a fairly specialised form of squelch, usually found on more expensive sets. It works in a very different way to carrier and deviation muting, in which the actual triggering takes place when any incoming signal is detected. Voice squelch needs not only an incoming signal but also speech or other form of modulation. This means it will not respond to a plain carrier signal. One of the main uses for this kind of squelch is to avoid locking onto oscillations generated within the scanner itself, known as 'birdies'. They appear to the scanner as a carrier wave and the simplest way to check for their presence is to unplug the aerial. If a 'carrier wave' is still present then it is a birdie. They can be a nuisance when searching between frequencies but with voice squelch, the scanner will ignore them. One tip, when listening to simplex transmissions, is to also insert 'delay' (see the following control) otherwise the scanner will carry on searching even when it has found a transmission.

Squelch delay

This is a feature only found on more expensive scanners and it allows the user to get the scanner to wait for a few seconds at the end of a transmission. Normally, once a station has sent its message, the transmission ceases and the scanner starts searching again. This can be a nuisance in some circumstances. Say, for instance, you are trying to listen to a conversation between two stations but each time one of them stops transmitting to let the other station reply, your scanner zooms off through the rest of its channels. At best you have to wait for the scanner to come back to the channel, by which time you will have missed part of the conversation and at worst you will miss everything else because your scanner locks onto a transmission on another channel.

With squelch delay it is possible to get the scanning circuit to wait for a few seconds, to see if there is going to be another transmission, before starting to scan other channels.

Obviously this facility is only needed with single frequency simplex transmission (amateur, aircraft, some marine channels, etc). There, both stations are on the same frequency or channel. Squelch delay is not required with split frequency simplex: in that case you would want the scanner to get as quickly as possible to the other channel where the second station will transmit its reply.

On some scanners it is possible to program the delay facility into memory along with the channel frequency so that delay occurs only on required channels.

Pre-set squelch

While most scanners allow the user to adjust the point at which the squelch opens and closes, some smaller sets such as pocket portables have a pre-set squelch control. This usually takes the form of a small trimming component on the circuit board rather than the rotary or slider resistor type provided as a front panel control. Be warned, though, that it is not a good idea to go delving inside your scanner to adjust this control unless you know what you are doing. Failure to ignore this warning could be expensive and your scanner would not be the first to arrive back at a service workshop in need of complete re-alignment because the wrong trimmers have been 'tweaked'.

Squelch override, squelch defeat, mute defeat

Featured on scanners with pre-set squelch, a push button which manually opens the squelch circuit. Useful if the signal is very weak or varying in reception strength.

Using squelch

The normal variable squelch found on most scanners must be used properly. On turning the squelch control gently there will come a point where the background noise suddenly disappears — this is the ideal squelch setting. If the control is turned further stronger and stronger signals are required to open the squelch circuit. Some of the channels stored in memory will have a higher background noise than others, so if the squelch keeps opening on a dead channel merely increase the setting slightly, to compensate, allowing the scanner to step through the complete scanning range. However, never set the squelch any higher than you have to. Winding it to full will almost certainly block out all but the very strongest of signals.

Some squelch circuits have 'hysteresis'. This means there is a slight difference in sensitivity between their 'on' and 'off' points. It becomes noticeable when the scanner stops on a signal but the squelch does not close again when the signal disappears. Again it is simply a question of advancing the control slightly to overcome the effect.

Automatic noise limiter (ANL)

A switch which minimises the effects of pulse-type interference, such as the interference caused by ignition circuits in cars.

Automatic frequency control (AFC)

This circuit is rarely encountered on scanners but is sometimes found on special monitor receivers. It is a circuit that will automatically track slight changes in frequency by the transmitting station. It is particularly useful on receivers designed for satellite reception. Orbiting satellites travel at high speed and signal reception may be therefore subject to what is known as 'Doppler shift' — an apparent change in received frequency AFC will track the tuning for these slight changes.

Auto-write scan

Allows the scanner to search all channels between two pre-set frequencies (normal search) and if it comes across any transmission the frequency of the channel is memorised.

Bandwidth

You will recall that earlier in the book (Chapter 2) we explained that different kinds of transmission take up different bandwidths, eg, communications transmissions are quite narrow while broadcast transmissions are relatively wide. Most scanners are designed to receive narrow bandwidth channels although in some cases they may switch automatically to slightly wider bandwidths at UHF. This is because UHF channels are spaced slightly further apart than VHF ones. Some of the newer scanners on the market do offer the option of switching to the kind of wide bandwidth needed to listen to broadcast transmissions and some sets even go as far as allowing the required bandwidth to be programmed for each individual channel stored in the memory.

Selector buttons are usually marked NFM, NAM (or just AM) and WFM, where N stand for 'narrow' and W stands for 'wide'.

Clear (M–clear)

This switch clears all data such as frequency, mode, etc, in memory, so freeing the memory and allowing the user to program new data in.

Dial

On some scanners this transfers control from the automatic up/down search to the manual tuning control knob.

Dial to memory (D ▷ M)

On scanners with a manual tuning control this allows a frequency that has been manually tuned-in to be entered into memory at the press of a button.

Down (▽)

Instructs the scanner to search downwards in frequency. See also 'UP' control.

Enter

Instructs the scanner to put information into memory.

Fine tune

Many synthesised scanners have a small fine tuning control which allows tuning slightly to either side of the centre frequency of the channel — useful when a transmitter is sending a signal slightly off-frequency from normal. Occasionally, it can be used to receive an FM signal while the scanner is in AM mode. By tuning to the side of the FM signal we tune slightly into the side-band allowing the scanner to resolve the signal by a 'slope detection' method.

Full tuning

This feature has only recently appeared on some sets and is an addition to the more familiar search mode. An example of this facility is seen on the Yaesu-Musen scanner and it looks like a normal tuning knob. In fact it is a clever rotary switch which allows the user to manually tune up or down, allowing the user to search around channels at his own pace rather than at the normal search stepping speed. Many people still prefer the feel of a conventional tuning knob and this facility does provide it. A nice extra if you can afford a set with it on (Yaesu, AOR2002, Icom).

Key lock
Disables the keyboard so that settings cannot be accidentally disturbed.

Lock-out
There may be times when the scanner owner wants to listen to only a few of the channels that he has programmed into memory. In cases like this it is possible on some scanners to miss out those channels that are not required. This is accomplished by using 'lock-out'. The method employed varies with different scanners but usually takes one of two forms. On simple crystal controlled scanners each channel may simply have a switch which brings that channel into the scan or leaves it out. On synthesised scanners the principle is similar but usually done by a keyboard command rather than individual switches.

The second variation is where the scanner has two scanning sequences. One includes all the channels in the memory but the other includes only certain channels that are selected by the keyboard. This second search pattern, often called 'search B', can include as few or as many memory channels as required.

Manual
Allows the user to stop the scanner and use it instead to monitor a channel not in memory. On some sets the 'manual' control also tells the scanner to get ready to memorise a new channel frequency.

Memory count
Available on the Bearcat 250, it counts the number of times the scanner stops on a particular channel. The number can be recalled and so provide a useful guide as to which channels are the most 'active' in an area.

Memory to dial (M ▷ D)
This allows a channel frequency in memory to be recalled at the press of a button and for manual tuning to then be available to tune up or down from that frequency. Useful, for example, if the scanner is tuned to a channel in one band and the user wishes to re-tune to another band — simply pressing the button associated with a channel in the desired band does the job.

Mode selector

Some scanners will only operate in one mode. For instance 2 metre amateur and marine band scanners only receive FM while scanners designed solely for the aircraft band only receive AM. Even some synthesised scanners such as those in the Bearcat range do not allow the user to select the mode even though they cover both AM and FM channels: the circuit automatically switches to AM or FM depending on which band the scanned channel is in. Some scanners allow the user to choose between AM or FM, but do not allow reception of AM *and* FM channels in one scan. A typical example is the SX-200 which has a simple AM/FM switch on the front panel. The disadvantage here is that the scanner cannot properly receive, say, both marine (FM) *and* aircraft (AM) bands together in one scan.

However, some scanners (the SX-400 and AORs, Yaesu, Realistic PRO-2004 and Icom are typical examples) allow the user to program each memory channel not only with the channel frequency but also the mode.

Priority channel (PRI, PRIO)

This feature allows one channel to be programmed as a prime or priority channel. In other words, during the scan sequence, the priority channel is scanned more times than the others. A typical scan sequence on such receivers would be: scan channel 1 — scan priority — scan 2 — scan priority scan 3, etc. An example of the use of this facility is when scanning the marine band where channel 16 (which is the calling and distress channel) could be scanned more than the others. Some scanners allow the user to decide which channel will have priority, whereas others, such as the AORs, always assume channel 1 as the priority channel.

Readouts, dials and lights

Simple crystal controlled scanners rarely incorporate anything more elaborate than a small LED lamp for each channel to show which one is actually being received when scanning stops. However synthesised scanners usually have some means of providing more information. A typical type of readout is a digital one showing not only the received frequency but also the number of the memory channel into which it is programmed. Obviously frequency readout is very important where a scanner with search facilities is concerned as without it it would be impossible to ever know where to look again for any station that you came across.

A scanner's digital readout of frequency is very accurate and some users rely on them as measuring instruments, for checking the frequency of transmitting equipment.

RF attenuator (ATT)
Also sometimes marked as a local/dx switch, this allows the scanner to be desensitised. The main use of this switch is to stop strong signals from nearby transmitters from causing interference.

Scan rate
This is a control which allows the speed at which the scanner steps through the scan sequence to be changed.

Search stop
Found on the Bearcat 250: the scanner searches until a transmission is received, but does not resume searching when the transmission stops. This allows the user time to check the frequency and put it into memory.

Signal meter (S meter)
A facility only found on more expensive sets which measures the strength of the incoming signal. It can be used in conjunction with fine tuning controls to ensure that the transmission is accurately tuned and is also a good way of checking on what conditions are like due to such things as the weather by keeping a check on the signal strength of, say, a known distant beacon transmitter. It can also be used for checking out the effectiveness of different kinds of aerial by comparing the received signal strengths from a reference source such as a beacon.

There are two main types of signal meter; a bargraph type consisting of a row of LED lights or a conventional moving coil meter with a pointer.

Step
Found on simple crystal controlled scanners, this is a push button that allows the channels in memory to be stepped through manually. Useful to stop the scan and set the receiver to stay on one particular channel.

Step rate (search rate)
Some scanners allow a degree of control over their stepping rate in the search mode. If you imagine the search facility as a sort of tuning knob that is automatically being turned for you then you get a rough idea of how search works. However, unlike a conventional tuning control which is fully variable, a scanner's search facility moves up or down in small steps. Typical steps are 12.5 kilohertz per step at VHF and 25 kilohertz per step at UHF. Most synthesised scanners set these rates automatically for whichever band they are scanning, as they are typical of the channel spacing for those bands. However, some more expensive sets allow you to set your own stepping rate. For scanners capable of receiving SSB transmissions this is vital because of the tuning accuracy required — these scanners need to have stepping rates as low as 100 hertz.

Up (△)

In search mode this tells the scanner to tune upwards in frequency. Like the DOWN (▽) control it is a search command.

Inputs and outputs

All scanners need connections for incoming and outgoing signals. For instance, we have to get radio signals in and so need a socket for the aerial. Next, having plugged an aerial to the scanner, we may well be content to listen to received transmissions on the built-in loudspeaker. However, even the simplest of scanners usually offers at least some kind of socket for either an external loudspeaker or earpiece.

Audio outputs

The quality of loudspeakers built into most scanners is usually defined as a compromise between cost and space saving. Even pocket-sized scanners can be improved on, when used at home, by plugging them into a bigger external speaker. Bigger scanners will also benefit from being run into a good quality loudspeaker which will give far clearer audio.

Another form of audio output found on some sets is the 'record' socket. This provides a low-level output (not amplified enough to feed a loudspeaker) which can be fed either to a tape recorder or separate amplifier. That secondary use can be useful in noisy environments where the scanner's internal amplifier is not powerful enough to provide enough volume. For instance, the early version of the SX-200 (prior to the 200N series) had an output that could barely be heard in a noisy vehicle. Several owners used a small separate amplifier giving a few watts output to solve the problem.

This socket can obviously also be used for recording transmissions (remember the warning at the front of the book though) and its output usually remains at a constant level which is not affected by the setting of the scanner's volume control.

Switching control

This is a refinement found on some expensive scanners. It is an electronic switch which is coupled to the squelch and switches on when a signal is present. It is used mostly to turn a tape recorder on and off so that transmissions during scanning can be recorded without wasting tape. A useful facility, but be warned that sets such as the SX-200 have such a connection but still need a small external control circuit to do the switching ... in other words you cannot just plug your recorder's remote control plug into the scanner.

Computer control

This is an input/output socket, usually configured as a serial interface, which allows a scanner to be controlled externally by a home computer. It is a facility found on only the most expensive scanners and the adaptor to connect to the computer is an optional extra. Connection is usually via the home computer's V24 (sometimes called: RS232C) port. With such a system, massively increased control over the scanner's functions is possible using relatively simple software. For instance, it becomes possible to increase the number of memories available, as well as adding sophisticated controlling sequences. In some cases it is possible to devote a memory 'page' in the computer to hold channel frequency mode and bandwidth details as well as store user's notes about the channel.

The point about computer control is that all scanner functions become controllable by the user, via a computer keyboard and controlling programs. The user is no longer limited by the functions, features and sequences which the manufacturer builds into the scanner, but can now define his own. Computer control is one of the biggest steps forward in scanner technology over recent years.

IF output

This is a connection socket usually found on scanners, such as the SX-400, aimed at the professional market. It allows the user to tap into the intermediate frequency (IF) section of the scanner's circuit. Such sockets are normally used to allow the intermediate frequency waveform to be examined on test instruments such as oscilloscopes, and they also allow the signal to be processed in other ways for other modes such as SSB and telemetry. On the SX-400, the facility allows SSB to be resolved if a communications-type HF receiver is available. The output is merely taken to the HF receiver's aerial socket and the receiver is then tuned to 10.7MHz (the SX-400's IF output frequency). By switching to SSB mode the HF receiver is then used merely as an IF amplifier/detector.

The Icom R7000 also has a fully buffered 10.7MHz IF output which can be used with eternal demodulators or an oscilloscope. I have also successfully used this socket on my own R7000 to feed an external IF amplifier/demodulator with 50KHz bandwidth for weather satellite reception (the circuit is an inexpensive kit available from Cirkit, part number 40-97020) but you will need to replace the two filters supplied with narrower SFA10.7MF types (also from Cirkit, part number 16-10760).

Operating your scanner 4

Some scanners are fairly easy to operate, others not so. Operation is a task that, often, is not helped when the instruction manual seems to be written in pidgin English — usually a strange cross between Japanese and Americanese. In my opinion, a classic example of a poorly written manual is that supplied with early SX-200s, which earned a reputation among owners as one of the most baffling documents ever produced. However, whatever the quality of instruction manual, the owner should at least *try* to understand it, as failure to know how the equipment works will at best frustrate the operation and at worst lead to serious damage.

Synthesised scanners

These fall into two distinct categories; internally and externally programmed. Internally programmed scanners are merely one step better than crystal controlled scanners, in that they are programmed to scan through a series of pre-selected channel frequencies and do no more than that. Indeed, the only real advantage over the crystal controlled type is; if you find a particular channel is not of great interest it is a simple matter to re-program the scanner without going to the expense of buying more crystals.

The externally programmed synthesised scanner offers far more versatility. Typical of this type are the Bearcats, SX series, Yaesu-Musen, Icom, etc. Normally these scanners not only allow scanning of normal pre-determined channels but also have search facilities.

Searching

Let us imagine a situation. You are not familiar with VHF or UHF communications but you have bought a synthesised scanner and although you know what you want to listen to, you are not sure what frequencies such transmissions are on in your area. For instance, you may wish to monitor the transmissions from your local airport. A look at some bandplans such as those in Chapter 7 of this book will tell you that voice transmissions in the main aircraft band are located between 118 and 136MHz and are transmitted in AM mode. Now you have a rough idea where to look but still no idea of the exact frequencies that you may want. On most synthesised scanners it should now be a fairly simple matter to find the frequencies you want although it may take a little patience. First, you need to get your scanner to *search* between 118 and 136MHz. The handbook for your equipment will tell you how to set the limit of the lowest and highest frequency of the band you wish to hunt through. Depending on the set, you may also need to select AM mode reception although on some models, such as the Bearcats, AM will automatically be selected when you tune to these frequencies.

Once you have got the scanner searching it is merely a question of waiting until you hear the transmissions you want. As the scanner stops on such transmissions you must be ready to make a note of the channel frequency that is shown on the readout. You may require several such frequencies in the example we have given as, for instance, most airports of any size usually transmit on a number of frequencies; at least one for the approach controller and at least one for the control tower.

Once you have found and made a note of all the frequencies in the particular band you have been searching you should then stop the scanner and enter those frequencies into memory.

Memory scanning

Having searched for channel frequencies, found them and entered them into memory we then go on to true scanning: where the equipment is set to step, one by one, through each channel to see if anything is being transmitted.

For general listening it is likely that all the available channels will be scanned. However, there may be occasions when some channels are not required — possibly because they are very busy — and locking-on to them prevents hearing other channels that are of more interest. In this case it is possible to lock-out the unwanted channels. There are usually two methods of doing this. On scanners like the Bearcats and AORs it is possible to lock-out channels individually. This means that at any time a locked-out channel may be returned back into the scanning sequence. On the scanners, like the SX-200, it may not be possible to manipulate the channels individually. What happens is that two scanning sequences are set up. One, *scan A,* scans *all* the available memory channels. However, any of those channels can be designated as a secondary channel. In that case, *scan B* may be selected and any channel that has been designated as secondary will *not* be scanned. In other words you set up a complete bank of locked-out channels which is switched in or out of the scan sequence.

As a point of interest to newcomers, it's worth remembering that, very often, a transmission is encountered after it has started — you may even only hear the last word or two. What has happened is that the transmission was started while your scanner was checking through other channels. Also, bear in mind that while your scanner is monitoring one transmission you may well be missing another transmission on another channel. These may seem obvious but it is surprising how many scanner owners, initially at least, have some difficulty grasping these points.

Base stations

Most synthesised scanners are used as a base station, that is, permanently sited, rather than mobile as in a vehicle. There is no particular difficulty in setting up a base station installation, but do bear in mind the comments in Chapter 5 on aerials.

There are a few points to remember when locating the scanner. Always avoid places where there are extremes of temperature, moisture or dampness. It is also not advisable to locate the scanner in the vicinity of other equipment such as television sets. Strong electromagnetic fields around a TV can be picked up as an annoying buzz, by the scanner. Other forms of interference may also be a problem in certain locations — these are dealt with in more detail later in this chapter.

Mobile operation

Nearly all scanners can be used in a vehicle with a standard 13.8 volt supply with negative earth chassis. Most scanners are supplied with a bracket for this purpose and it is simply a question of fitting this bracket, with self-tapping screws, into a suitable location in the vehicle.

When deciding where to put the scanner in the vehicle take note of a few points. First, do not site it in front of hot air vents. The high temperature will certainly not do the scanner any good and, indeed, it may be high enough to damage any plastics that may have been used in the scanner's construction.

Second, note that unless you intend using an extension loudspeaker, you will need to make sure the scanner's loudspeaker is not obstructed. Most scanners only have about 1 watt audio output. In a quiet room that may seem more than adequate but it is barely enough in a car. An inexpensive external speaker can help tremendously (see Chapter 6, on accessories).

Finally, always bear in mind that there are thieves about. Not so many years ago specialised equipment such as scanners and amateur gear could be left in a vehicle because the average thief knew he would have little chance of selling it. Nowadays the situation has changed; there is a large and ready market. The answer to this is to either hide the scanner away or remove it altogether when the vehicle is left unattended. One way this can be done is by fitting the scanner to a sliding mount of the type often used for CB equipment. The mount, complete with scanner, can be removed in seconds and locked away in the boot, or even carried with you.

Portables

Until recently, the only portables available in Britain were the small crystal controlled scanners and these usually fell into three categories: marine and 2 metre amateur band, aircraft band or dual-banders.

The 2 metre amateur band is between 144 and 146MHz while the marine band between 156 and 162MHz. These two bands are very close and so it is usually quite a simple matter to re-tune a scanner tuned to one band so that it receives the other band — always assuming, of course, that you replace the crystals with ones for the new frequencies. Circuit diagrams are supplied with more scanners and anyone with a reasonable ability to recognise the relevant parts of the circuit should know what to trim. But a word of warning to the non-technical. Should you upset trimming controls in other parts of the circuit it is virtually impossible to get the scanner working properly again, without specialist test equipment.

Choosing crystals

Most people, when buying a crystal controlled scanner, specify the channels they want to cover, at the time of purchase. However, an owner may later wish to change crystals, but this might not be as straightforward as it first appears.

Although crystals are remarkably stable (that is, they do not vary much in oscillating frequency), they rarely oscillate *exactly* at the specified frequency. In the scanner, small trimmer capacitors allow fine adjustment of crystal oscillation frequency to allow exact setting. Ideally crystal trimming is a job you should leave to an expert with measuring equipment, but if you are really stuck, it is possible to do it approximately by ear. Tune the scanner to a fairly weak signal and then adjust the trimmer for minimum background hiss or noise.

Should you want to get crystals for standard bands, eg, marine, amateur or aircraft bands, these can usually be bought, over the counter, from dealers. On the other hand, should you want to tune to other bands, you may need to specially order crystals. You also need to be sure of a number of other factors.

First, you must be sure that the scanner can cope with the bands you want to tune. For instance, it's no use trying to tune say 88 MHz on a scanner designed to operate solely at 144MHz and above. The signal amplifying circuits just wouldn't be able to cope even if you re-trimmed them. The next thing you will need to know is the intermediate frequency of the scanner which on most scanners is 10.7MHz. This information should be in the instruction manual, where you should also find details of what kind of crystal you will need. Crystals are rarely made to oscillate at the actual frequency required — they are usually made instead for a much lower frequency which, when multiplied by a specified whole number will give the wanted frequency. The tuning circuits in the scanner do the multiplying, but *you* need to know by what number. Your handbook will either say something like '5th overtone crystal' or will show a formula along the lines of: 'crystal = desired frequency minus 10.7, divided by 5.' You must let the crystal supplier have this information as well as whether the crystal operates in *series* or *parallel* mode which again will be specified in your handbook. If this information is not to hand you will have to go back to your dealer who should be able to supply it.

Ordering crystals
You need to know:

1 The required frequency minus the IF frequency.
2 Which overtone.
3 Series or parallel mode.

You may be able to order a crystal from your dealer but if not they can often be obtained through mail order companies who advertise in magazines aimed at the amateur radio market.

Using a portable

Portables are obviously intended to be carried around and a consequence of this is that a frequent shortcoming is the aerial, which must be small. It is usually a short telescopic aerial or even, in some cases, just a short length of loose wire terminated in a small jack plug. The latter often provides poor performance and if better range is required is best replaced by either a telescopic aerial or, a helical aerial (often referred to as a 'rubber duck'). Note, though, that the aerial used needs to be designed for the frequency that will be covered by the scanner — in other words a CB band aerial will not produce good results if the scanner is tuned to another band. For more specific information on this topic, refer to Chapter 5.

Whatever kind of portable is being used, the positioning of the aerial is important. A scanner carried in the pocket close to the body will have poor pick-up because the sheer mass of the body will upset the characteristics of the aerial and in some cases will screen it from signals. It is also important that the aerial is in what is known as the right polarisation 'plane': most communication signals at VHF and UHF are transmitted from vertically polarised aerials and so the scanner aerial needs to be vertically polarised, too. Where possible therefore, the scanner's aerial should be kept clear of the body and the aerial, usually upright.

Portables in vehicles

There is no reason why a portable scanner can't be used in a vehicle, but don't expect good results if you are just using the portable's own aerial. Vehicle bodies provide a very effective screen, preventing good reception and so for best results an external aerial is necessary. One quick way of providing this facility is to use an aerial that has a magnetic base, so that it can be put in position and removed whenever desired, without the need to drill holes in the bodywork. Again, specific details are given in Chapter 5.

Power for the scanner can be either from the scanner's internal batteries, or from the vehicle's power circuit, through a suitable adaptor. Make sure the adaptor is the right one for the voltage required by the portable. Often scanner manufacturers will offer these adaptors, sometimes called 'power converters', as an optional accessory. Typically they consist of a small box of electronics with a lead at one end to plug into the scanner and a lead at the other end to plug into the vehicle's cigar lighter. A word of caution though on some other types. Many of the cheaper adaptors can draw quite heavy current — even when the scanner is not being used. So, if you intend to wire the adaptor permanently into the vehicle's power circuit you must be able to switch the adaptor off when you are not using the scanner, otherwise it will unnecessarily drain the vehicle's battery.

Beware —charger or supply

It is vitally important when connecting an external supply to a portable scanner that the supply is of the correct type, otherwise irreparable damage may occur to the scanner. Some scanners have a socket for an external supply, labelled something like 'DC6V'. Other scanners may have a socket labelled 'charge'. Some scanners may have both, or different sockets.

DC supply

This socket is intended for you to run the set from a suitable direct current power source at the specified voltage. Some portables also have a small circuit built into them that will also use that current to charge internal cells. Your manual should tell you this.

Charge

This socket is *not* intended for an external supply. The re-chargeable cells in the scanner require a specially controlled re-charging current so that they charge up at the correct rate. Putting an uncontrolled current into this socket, even at the right voltage, will cause the cells to charge far too quickly and could damage them. In some instances this can also be a cause of overheating, which can damage other components in the scanner, too.

Polarity

If you intend using a mains adaptor that was not made by the scanner manufacturer you must ensure that the plug fitted to the adaptor is wired the same way round as the socket on the scanner. The fact that the adaptor has the right plug to fit the scanner's socket does not mean that the socket and plug's positive and negative contacts match.

Interference

Scanners, like a lot of other radio receivers, may be upset by various types of 'man-made' interference. Typical examples of interference sources are home appliances that contain electric motors, and home computers. When using your scanner in the home it is a good idea to keep it well away from such items. It is also advisable not to site your scanner on top of a television set which can also generate strong electromagnetic signals. Most interference sources in the home can be minimised — you can always turn the TV or vacuum cleaner off. On the other hand, users living close to industrial sites may find that nearby machinery causes persistent problems. There are several courses of action that can be taken.

First, make sure that your own installation is not inviting problems. A good, high, outside aerial sited well away from machinery and fed through good quality coaxial cable of the correct impedence (see Chapter 5) may well cure the problem. Many scanners have a connection on the rear apron for an earth and in some cases a wire connected between this point and a copper spike inserted into the ground may make a significant difference.

If this fails to resolve the problem then you may be faced with somewhat more drastic action. In most countries it is an offence to radiate strong signals from machinery which is not fitted with adequate suppression. In such cases it is usually advisable, if you are sure who the culprit is, to make a friendly and tactful approach and try and get the owner of the interference source to sort the problem out. If this fails then you can of course approach the necessary authority, which in the UK is the local post office, and ask them to investigate the matter. However, be warned that if you are complaining because someone is interfering with your *illegal* listening activities, then the authorities will take a very dim view of your complaint.

In the case of a base station, another source of interference may cause problems. Sometimes, persistent interference can be transmitted along mains wiring — there is quite an easy way to test for this. Obtain a battery of the required voltage and power the scanner off this source: in most cases a car battery will do nicely. If the scanner does not suffer from interference when run off the battery, then you know that the problem is being transmitted along the mains wiring and there are two ways that the interference can now be eliminated.

First, the scanner can be permanently run from batteries, but bear in mind that most synthesised scanners draw quite a heavy current. An automobile battery may be alright, but it will be necessary to recharge it when the scanner is not in use. If such batteries and a charger are available then obviously this is an easy way to tackle the problem. However, there is another and neater solution. It is possible to buy special interference eliminators that plug into a normal domestic supply socket. The most recent types consist of a small box with a plug on one side and matching socket on the other. They contain electronics to remove interference spikes from the domestic AC supply and, once plugged-in, the scanner's mains voltage adaptor is then plugged into the socket on the rear of the unit. Interference eliminators are often used, too, by computer users in cases where their computers suffer from mains-borne interference.

Vehicle interference
All vehicles generate some level of interference from their electrical circuits and in some cases this can obliterate weak signals picked-up on a scanner in mobile use. Remember that mobile conditions are far from ideal anyway, and signals that are strong into a base station may well disappear below the level of vehicle ignition noise if some steps are not taken to reduce the problem.

Ignition noise
The first and most familiar type of interference, pulse noise, is caused by the vehicle's high tension ignition circuit. If this is excessive the first step is to fit a suppressor capacitor (specified for this type of interference) to the ignition coil. The coil will have three connections. The large thick

lead that goes to the distributor and two smaller leads, one marked 'CB' and the other 'SW'. The body clip of the suppressor capacitor must be connected to ground and the small flying lead must go to 'SW' (never connect to 'CB'). Ensure a good contact onto the chassis for the clip of the capacitor by scraping away any paintwork, rust, dirt, etc.

If this does not reduce interference to an acceptable level then you may need to replace the capacitor (if one exists) inside the distributor — it is not unknown for a capacitor to go open-circuit with age and no longer be effective.

You might never be able to completely eliminate this type of interference, but if it remains at a high level you should seek further advice from a garage.

If your vehicle is fitted with contactless electronic ignition you should refer to the vehicle handbook before attempting any kind of suppression. Some circuits of this type can cease to operate if fitted with capacitors.

Generator/alternator whine

As the name suggests this is a whining noise, heard through the receiver, that increases or decreases in pitch depending on the engine revs. It can get into the scanner in two ways; through the power supply lead or via the aerial.

It is simple to check which kind of problem is present by pulling out the aerial plug. If the sound persists then the interference is being transmitted along the power supply lead. A special device called an 'in-line choke' can be used to reduce this interference. Simply cut into the positive supply lead to the scanner and fit the choke in-line (they generally have simple screw connectors at both ends).

Often there is one further trick that sometimes dramatically reduces this kind of interference. Often the problem may be resolved by installing a power line to the scanner direct from the battery's positive terminal, by-passing the car's existing electrical wiring. The only problem that can arise is that if you leave the vehicle long enough and forget to switch the scanner off, then it will drain the battery.

If generator/alternator interference is entering the scanner via the aerial then a different kind of action is called for. In the case of a generator, a simple suppressor capacitor may be connected between the chassis and the generator's output lead. Note that you will need a capacitor designed for the job. In the case of an alternator, the solution really depends on the make and it is best to consult your car agent. The method of suppression is usually similar to that for a generator, particularly in the case of Lucas, Bosch and Delco types where the flying lead of the capacitor is connected to the terminal marked 'IND'.

Other interference

Instruments and equipment fitted in modern cars are usually quite well suppressed. However, older models may present interference problems from a variety of sources including: screen wiper motors, voltage regulators, instrument stabilisers, heater motor, indicator lights and stop lights. The most common cause of interference is the wiper motor, which, fortunately, is quite easy to identify — for obvious reasons. Often a simple solution to the problem is to connect a wire between the metal body of the motor and the chassis of the car (many of these motors 'float' on rubber buffers).

As for the other sources of interference mentioned, then specialist suppliers can provide the necessary suppressors specially designed for the job. In the UK the nearest dealer for Lucas parts can supply a wide range of suppressors. Lucas manufactures a device to suit virtually every kind of suppression problem.

General tips

One further method of reducing interference is known as 'bonding'. Many cars often have poor electrical contact between the engine bonnet and the engine compartment. This could mean that the bonnet does not screen all interference generated around the engine. A cure for this can be to use a bonding strap, consisting of copper braid. One end is connected to the chassis and the other to the bonnet (usually onto one of the bolts that holds the hinge mechanism). However, the strap *must* connect onto good, clean, bared metal, to give perfect electrical contact.

Sometimes, taking one step to reduce interference appears to have little effect. However, do not undo the work you have done. Carry on adding other methods of suppression. The real trick to 'quietening your car down' is to carry out steps that reduce the noise, little by little. It is rare that there is any 'miracle cure' where fitting one suppressor suddenly solves all your problems.

Flutter

This is not actually interference, but can be a problem with mobile working. The effect is a fluttering in the strength of the received signal. The biggest cause of this effect is the aerial swinging around on the vehicle. As the whip moves in relation to the body of the car its sensitivity to radio signals changes. They only real cure for this is to use a very stiff aerial. Swishy whip aerials may look very flash, but can cause terrible flutter.

Scanner tricks

Some synthesised scanners such as some Bearcat models can be made to tune outside their normal tuning ranges. Tricks like this are not really necessary with full coverage scanners such as the AORs, Yaesu and Icom but can be very useful with those receivers which do not cover certain frequencies.

However, although it is possible to trick some sets into working outside their normal range, it should be remembered that the further out of range they go then the more the sensitivity starts to fall off. This is because the tuning and amplifying circuits were not designed for this coverage.

Details of the Bearcat 220 and 250 are given here but I must scotch a rumour about the SX-200. This scanner cannot be made to receive outside its quoted coverage. I know this for a fact because I have actually been able to get my own SX-200 to appear as if it was tuning out of range ... in other words the frequency readout showed that it was. I will not bother to explain the procedure to achieve this because it is pointless. What happens is that, although the oscillator tuning circuits will go out of range, the moment this happens the signal amplifying stages switch off. It would appear that the internal microprocessor is programmed to switch-in one of the three signal amplifying heads, VHF low, VHF high and UHF, depending on where the set is tuned. However any attempt to get the synthesiser tuning out of range results in none of the amplifier heads being brought into circuit.

However, some trickery is available on two Bearcat models.

Bearcat 220FB

The gaps not covered by this scanner are 50—66MHz, 80—118MHZ, 136—144MHz and 174—420MHz. The latter gap covers such a wide range that the receiver will not operate over its entire span even when tricked into coverage. However, the other gaps can be easily covered with the following procedure. We will take the first gap, 50—66MHz as an example and you only need to substitute the other figures for the other gaps.

Use MANUAL to find a spare memory channel and then:

(1) Press 50   (5) Press LIMIT
(2) Press E   (6) Press SEARCH (ignore the ERROR signal)
(3) Press LIMIT   (7) Press LIMIT
(4) Press 66   (8) Press SEARCH

The scanner will now start to search upwards from 50MHZ.

Bearcat 250

A similar type of method is used to fill gaps in the coverage of the 250FB scanner. For instance this set does not normally cover the amateur 2 m band but will with the following sequence.

Find a clear or spare memory channel. Make sure the squelch is closed and then:

(1) Press 146
(2) Press LIMIT
(3) Press 146
(4) Press LIMIT
(5) Press STORE
(6) Open and close the squelch
(7) Press MANUAL

(8) Press 174
(9) Press LIMIT
(10) Press 174
(11) Press LIMIT
(12) Press SEARCH
(13) Press RECALL
(14) Press SEARCH

The set should search downwards in frequency from 146 to 133MHz.

To store a frequency , open the squelch just before reaching it and use the search button to step onto the frequency. Then, with the squelch still open switch the scanner off and then on again. The frequency should be stored in the appropriate memory.

SX-200

Having already said that it is not possible to carry out a similar procedure with the SX-200, there is a simple little sequence for this set which gets rid of the persistent clock. Owners of the SX-200 will know that this wretched clock is a nuisance when trying to monitor a single channel. Instead of the frequency being displayed the time pops up. It can be got rid of by a trick search process. Enter the frequency you want, press the LIMIT button, enter the frequency again and then press the SEARCH button. The set now tries to search between the two frequencies and as a result shows the same frequency all the time, albeit with a very slight flicker.

SX-400

Despite its impressive facilities and performance, the SX-400 does not have facilities for single sideband. However, it does have a socket on the back with 10.7MHz IF output, and if an HF communications type receiver is available then this can be used as an SSB IF strip. Simply connect the IF output to the antenna socket of the HF receiver and tune it to 10.7MHz. Turn the volume down on the scanner and listen on the HF set whilst tuning on the scanner.

Aerials 5

The terms 'aerial' and 'antenna' are synonymous, meaning that part of a radio system which radiates electromagnetic energy (a transmitting aerial) or picks-up electromagnetic energy (receiving aerial). An aerial, together with connecting cable, supports, etc, is known as an aerial system.

Forget the telescopic

Most scanners are provided with a telescopic aerial which is only of use to enable the scanner to receive strong transmissions from a nearby transmitter. To get the best out of your equipment and to be able to receive weaker transmissions you will need to invest in a proper aerial system — and why not? You have probably invested quite a considerable amount of hard-earned cash in your scanner and so it would be a shame not to get the best out of it just for the sake of a few more pounds. A reasonable aerial system does not need to cost a great deal of money.

When an external aerial is used the telescopic must be removed
Leaving the telescopic aerial plugged-in when also using an external aerial will upset the input stages of the scanner and the resulting mismatch will spoil reception. So, whenever you use an external aerial with your scanner, remember to disconnect the telescopic aerial.

VHF/UHF aerials

The use of aerials is something of a black art for the newcomer to VHF/UHF radio and the situation is not helped by the fact that there are a great many types to choose from. They basically fall, however, into two distinct types; broadband or narrow band.

Before proceeding further, though, we should consider some of the basic principles of VHF/UHF aerial design because they vary greatly from those of aerials used at HF and lower frequencies. For instance, one common myth amongst many non-technical people is that 'the bigger the aerial the better'. It is not unknown for some first time scanner buyers to try and improve reception by using long lengths of wire with one end poked into the scanner's aerial socket. Not only will this not improve reception but will probably produce even poorer results than the simple telescopic aerial. The simple reason for this is that at VHF/ UHF frequencies, aerials must be of the correct dimensions. A typical example, will be familiar to most people, is the UHF television aerial. Notice how the width of the aerials in your area are all pretty much the same — the length varies according to the number of elements on the boom of the aerial but the width remains constant. That is because they are all tuned to pick up the same transmitter.

Polarisation (Figures 5.1 and 5.2)

Having considered the importance of physical dimensions of aerials we must also consider polarisation. The 'quarter-wave' whip example is typical of a vertically polarised aerial. All that means is that the whip or main element of the aerial is upright and, in practice, will only be suitable for receiving signals from aerials which are also vertically polarised. Some types of aerial, though, are horizontally polarised. They operate in a plane that is parallel to the ground. These are rarely used for mobile communications as they are directional and literally have to be pointed

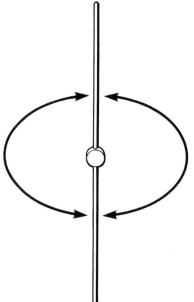

Figure 5.1 Vertical polarisation. Pick up pattern is in all directions.

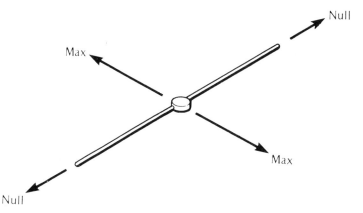

Figure 5.2 Horizontal polarisation. The antenna is sensitive in two directions on and picks up very little end-on.

at the signal source. Horizontally polarised aerials are frequently used for communications between two fixed points.

Virtually all aerial designs can be used vertically polarised but some designs, such as quarter-wave whips and 'discones', do not readily lend themselves to horizontal operation. There are some other forms of polarisation, namely 'slant' and 'circular', but these rarely apply to scanners and so are not dealt with here.

Narrow band aerials

Whips (Figure 5.3)

Let us now look at practical designs of whips. First, the quarter-wave whip. It is essentially a narrow band aerial although in fact, in reception, will operate with fair performance over a wide range of frequencies. For instance, an aerial cut for 100MHz will provide reasonable reception from about 50 to 200MHz. It is difficult to quote exact figures as a lot will depend on the strength of the signals in a given area.

The quarter-wave whip aerial lends itself to both mobile and base station use. Commercially available mobile whip aerial systems are usually sold in two parts: the whip itself which is cut by the purchaser to whatever length required and a mounting unit. The mounting unit can take the form of a 'through body mounting', fitted in a similar way to a normal car radio aerial system. Another mounting unit consists of a small clamp, attached to the water drain gutter above the car doors. This fitting obviously means that no holes have to be drilled in the car's bodywork. The need for drilling is again avoided when a magnetically-mounted aerial system is used, consisting of a large, powerful magnet covered in a rubber boot, on top of which is a small clamp to which the whip is connected. Such 'magmounts' are very popular these days

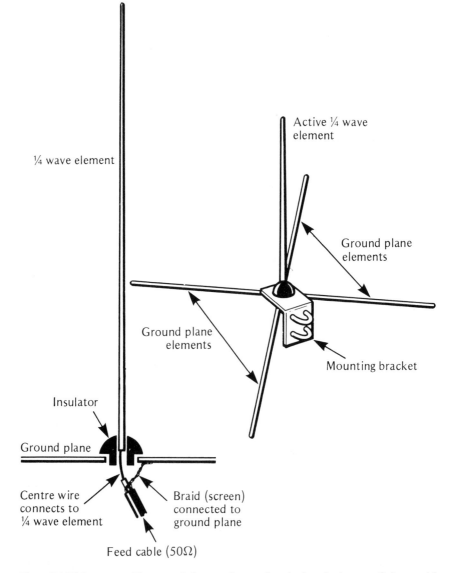

Figure 5.3 Whip antenna. The ground plane can be a steel car body or in the case of a base aerial can be ¼ wave long rods.

because they can easily be removed when the car is left unattended. This means the aerial is not at the mercy of vandals and it is not so obvious that valuable scanning equipment is installed.

In the case of mobile operation, the body of the car provides the 'ground plane', necessary for correct quarter-wave whip aerial functioning. In the case of a base aerial a ground plane is provided, usually, by four elements, each a quarter-wave or more in length.

Photograph 5(a) Typical ground plane aerial. This one is designed for airband and the 'drooping' radials give a better 50 Ohm match.

Dimensions

Remember, in Chapter 2, we saw that for any given radio frequency signal there is a corresponding wavelength. Well, when we talk of a quarter-wave aerial we are referring to the physical size of an aerial which is one quarter of the wavelength of the operating frequency. In practice, the whip length is around 5 per cent less. There is a simple mathematical formula to work this out: Quarter-wave aerial length = 71.5 divided by frequency (in MHz).

The resulting length is in metres. The story does not quite end there, because in order for the aerial to perform correctly it should have a ground plane. In the case of a base aerial this usually comprises metal rods connected to the earthing braid of the aerial cable at the base of the whip. In the case of mobile operation, the earthed metal bodywork of the vehicle acts as the ground plane.

In addition to the quarter-wave whip there are several variants, notably the ⅝ wave whips fitted with appropriate load coils.

Dipoles

The dipole (which also forms the basis of the Yagi aerial — see later) is the most commonly used aerial at VHF/UHF frequencies. It can take two forms; simple or folded. It is not normally used as a mobile aerial because of the difficulties of mounting it. However, it is used extensively as a base station aerial and, unlike the whip, does not require a ground plane as such.

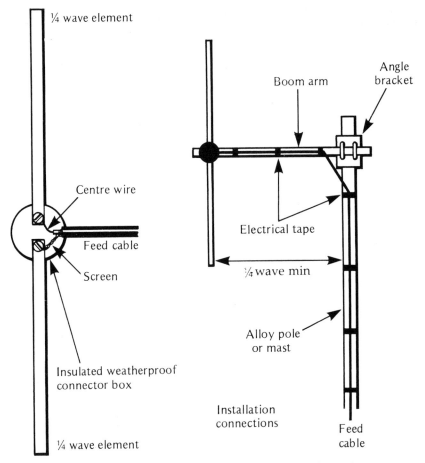

Figure 5.4 The dipole. Vertically polarised it provides good all round reception.

Let us look at a simple dipole which consists of just two elements, the active and the passive. Refer to Figure 5.4 and you will see that what we have, in effect, is two quarter-wave elements, one above the other. The dipole therefore is a half wavelength across. It can be mounted vertically polarised, which makes it omni-directional or horizontally polarised which makes it directional into two areas. Most scanner users, though, find the vertical version the most useful. The calculations for each element are the same as those given for the quarter wave-whip.

A variation on the simple dipole is known as the folded dipole where the outer ends of the two elements are looped across and connected to each other.

Yagis (Figure 5.5)

The Yagi is a dipole (usually folded) which has added elements to make it directional. Most television aerials are of Yagi construction. The folded dipole is mounted on a boom with a reflector element behind and

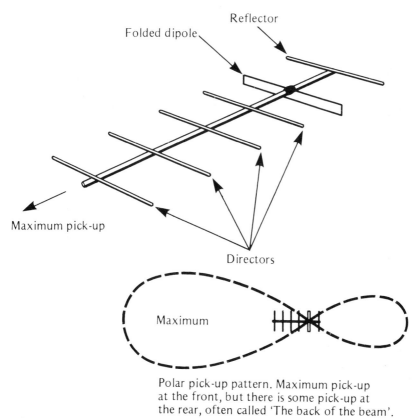

Polar pick-up pattern. Maximum pick-up at the front, but there is some pick-up at the rear, often called 'The back of the beam'.

Figure 5.5 The Yagi (beam)

director elements in front. The directional characteristic of the aerial and its gain varies according to the number of director elements. Yagi aerials are normally used for working between two fixed points and can be used either vertically or horizontally. Amateurs use Yagis for reception of long range VHF/UHF transmissions, but to do so successfully have to fit them with motorised aerial rotators; so the aerial can be pointed exactly at the transmitting aerial.

Photograph 5(b) An eight element Yagi operating in horizontal polarisation mode. The antenna is highly directional hence the rotator motor to turn it.

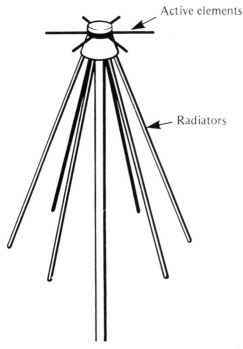

Active elements

Radiators

Figure 5.6 The Discone. Despite the horizontal top elements the aerial is vertically polarised and very broadband.

Broadband aerials

Discones (Figure 5.6)

This is the aerial of the greatest interest to the scanner owner who wants to tune over a wide range of frequencies. It is a very broadband aerial and some types will work quite effectively over the entire VHF/UHF bands.

It is not an aerial that readily lends itself to being home-made as it is quite complex in terms of the metalwork involved. It will only work as a vertically polarised aerial and is only really suitable as the basis of a base station aerial system. Commercially there are a number to choose from and prices range quite widely. However, as a simple guide it is best to go for one that has a large number of elements and preferably elements that are made of solid rod or seamless tube. Those made from thin seamed alloy tend to deteriorate very quickly in poor weather.

Photograph 5(c) The Discone. Easily the most popular broadband aerial amongst scanner users.

Aerials for portables

A hand-portable scanner can be used with virtually any type of mobile or base aerial and the consequent performance will be better than any small aerial that is normally attached directly to the scanner. However, use of such aerials defeats the portability feature of the scanner.

Some portable scanners are supplied with only a small length of wire to act as an aerial. These are probably the poorest aerials as they can rarely be kept in an upright position. A far better choice is the use of a telescopic or helical, and to this end most portable scanners have a socket frequently either a BNC type or miniature jack plug for an external aerial. By far the most common aerial used on portable scanners is the following.

Helicals (rubber ducks)

A helical aerial comprises a metal spring, shrouded in rubber or plastic. They are often seen on walkie-talkies and offer the advantage that unlike a telescopic they are flexible and not easily broken. In practice, the spring usually consists of a metal wire of ⅝th wavelength wound over a width of about 10mm. The top part is stretched out slightly but often the lower end is fairly close wound so as to provide correct impedance matching with the scanner.

Helicals offer better performance than the loose wire aerial, are very compact and portable, do not easily break and, being far shorter than

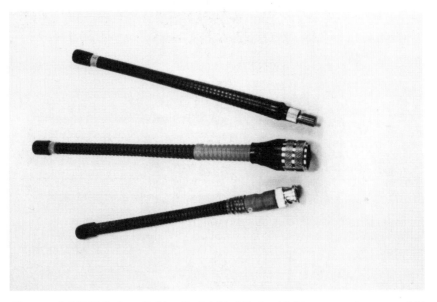

Photograph 5(d) Helicals or 'Rubber Ducks'. Ideal for hand held scanners, they are available with BNC PL259 and screw-in connectors.

respective telescopic aerials, are less likely to do personal damage like poking someone's eye out. However, it is likely that a telescopic aerial will give better performance.

Whatever kind of aerial is used, remember that if the scanner is kept in a pocket or any other position close to the body the performance will be reduced. Not only does the body act as a screen but the sheer mass can upset the aerial impedance. Portable scanners do not work very well inside vehicles or buildings. In each case it should be possible to attach an external aerial to the set to improve performance. In the case of mobile operation a magnetically mounted aerial is ideal.

Satellite aerials

Although reception of many satellite transmissions can easily be accomplished on fairly simple VHF/UHF equipment it presents a special problem in terms of aerials. Remember how earlier we discussed the problem of polarisation when we said that the transmitting and receiving

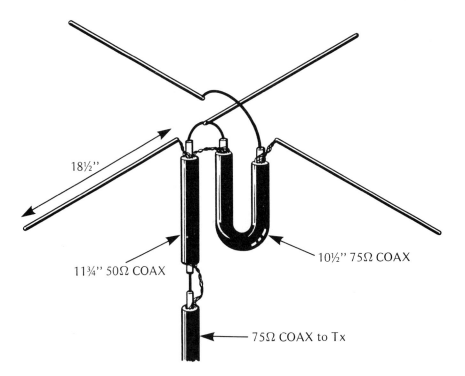

Figure 5.7 The feed arrangements for a 2m crossed dipole antenna. Each of the elements is 18½ inches long.

aerials must be phased the same way. The problem we face with satellite reception is that the satellite itself will not have an aerial that remains in the same phase. Orbiting satellites travel from horizon to horizon and their aerials will change position and vary in phase in relation to the aerial on the ground.

The effect of this is that signals from a satellite will appear to get louder and then slowly fade away before getting louder again and then again fading. The way to overcome this is to use what is known as a crossed dipole — effectively two dipoles with the resultant aerial having horizontal *and* vertical polarisation (Figure 5.7).

Simple and inexpensive crossed dipoles can be bought from Halbar Aerials and Jay-Beam, whose addresses are at the back of the book.

Cable

All base and mobile aerials need to be connected to the scanner using screened coaxial cable. However, any old cable that you have lying around might not be suitable. There are several types of coaxial cable available, some for aerials, others for audio and hi-fi use. The latter are unsuitable as are cables designed for use with a normal car radio.

The remaining aerial cables fall into two sections, 50 ohm and 75 ohm impedance types. Cable impedance is most critical. The 50 ohm variety is normally used to connect professional, commercial, amateur and CB aerials while 75 ohm cable is used for domestic VHF radio and television. You must use the right one for your scanner. The scanner instruction manual should tell you which cable impedance to use. Failing that the aerial socket on the set may be labelled with the impedance. If it is not shown then it is reasonably safe to assume that the correct cable is the 50 ohm type. A few older scanners do have 70 ohm inputs and in that case normal domestic TV coaxial cable can be used.

50 ohm cable is available from amateur and CB radio dealers but like the 75 ohm types two main kinds are available; normal or low-loss. If the scanner is only being used for VHF reception and only about 8 or 10 metres of cable is to be used then normal cable can be used. However, if UHF reception or long cable lengths are required then low loss cable is needed.

Cable construction
Whatever kind of coaxial cable you use, it will have roughly the construction shown in Figure 5.8. Starting at the middle is the core wire which carries the signal, shrouded in a plastic insulator. The insulator prevents the core from touching the outer braid, which is wound in such a way as to provide an earthed screen for the core. This screen serves two purposes: it ensures that the correct impedance is maintained along the

entire length of the cable; it stops any interference from reaching the inner core. Finally, the entire cable is covered in plastic insulation. It is important when installing an aerial that this outer insulation is intact and not torn or gouged so that the braid is exposed. Rainwater getting into the cable in such circumstances will almost certainly ruin the cable.

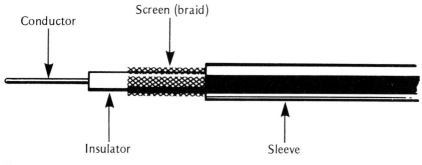

Figure 5.8 Coaxial cable.

As the screen of the cable is earthed, it is important when connecting the cable to either the aerial or the connector plug that the inner wire and the braid wire *never touch*. If they do, the incoming signal is earthed, and so lost.

Photograph 5(e) Simple crossed dipole for satellite reception. This one was made up from two old band 1 TV aerials. Note the phasing line taped to the mast.

Connectors

In order to plug the aerial cable into the scanner you will need appropriate connectors. If you intend to fit your own then note that you will need a soldering iron: twisted wires or wires poked into sockets will

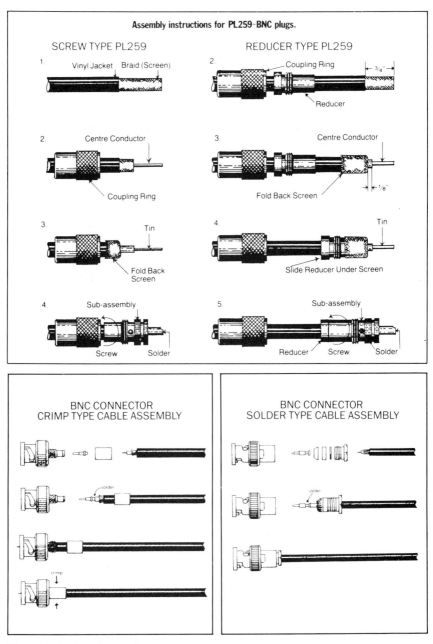

Figure 5.9 Various plugs and connectors.

almost certainly lead to signal losses. Several types of plug are in common use and are shown in Figure 5.9. It is also possible to purchase adaptors so that an aerial which has one type of plug can be connected to a scanner which takes another type.

PL259

Commonly found on CB sets and amateur equipment, PL259 connectors are only occasionally encountered on scanners, usually of the older variety. However, they are used extensively to connect to aerials. For instance a socket for a PL259 plug will be found on the base of most discones.

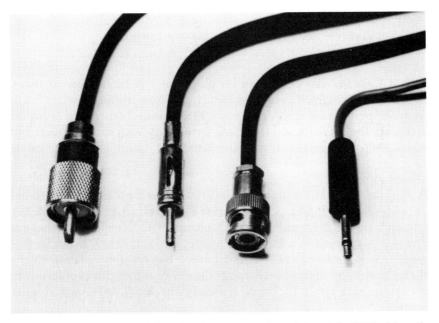

Photograph 5(f) Typical aerial plugs found on scanners. From left to right: PL259, Motorola, BNC and miniature jack. The latter is usually confined to hand held sets.

The plug comes in several varieties some of which are easier to fit than others. The simplest are designed for use with the thinner, standard (non-low-loss), cable. The cable is trimmed, about a quarter inch of braid is left and folded back over the outer insulator. The cable is then pushed into the plug and the braiding and insulator screwed into the plug's shell. Once fully home, the centre conductor is then soldered.

Other types of PL259 have a separate inner sleeve which is either a wide or narrow type depending on the coaxial cable used. This type of plug can be fitted to thicker, low-loss, cables and the appropriate sleeve is purchased separately. When fitting, the braid must be worked back over the sleeve. The inner conductor is then soldered in the normal way.

It is a good idea with both types of plug to expose more centre conductor than is needed. The surplus can be snipped off after soldering.

PL259 plugs have an outer shell that is internally threaded and when mated with the socket this shell is screwed up tight to ensure firm contact.

BNC

This connector is found on professional communication and test equipment and is much smaller than the PL259. However, it has a simple twist and pull action for release which makes it a lot quicker to change over than the PL259. This type of plug is used on some of the later scanners such as the AOR's. Unfortunately, its smaller dimensions make it more fiddly to attach to the cable. It is difficult to give specific instructions on fitting as construction differs greatly between makes.

Motorola

This is the car radio aerial type of plug that will be familiar to many people. Surprisingly in a way this low quality type of plug (low quality in terms of performance at VHF and UHF) is found on several scanners including the SX200N and Bearcats. Types vary with manufacturer but a look at the plug will usually make it clear how it is attached to the cable.

Miniature jack

A plug that is far from suited to VHF/UHF but it is occasionally found on some of the smaller portable crystal controlled scanners: probably chosen because it is small and very cheap. A look inside will make it obvious as to what is soldered to where, but a difficulty arises in that most miniature jack plugs do not have a big enough opening in the barrel to take 50 ohm coaxial cable. One way round this problem is to cut off the back end of the barrel with say, a hacksaw, so leaving a bigger opening.

Building an aerial

If you are not prepared to go to the expense of purchasing an expensive aerial such as a discone, it is possible to build a simple dipole, easily and cheaply. The job is made easier if you can lay your hands on an old Band 1 (BBC 405-line) TV aerial. A surprising number of these aerials still sit around in lofts unused in these days of UHF TV. If it *has* only been used inside then it will not have suffered from corrosion and will be eminently suitable for modification.

First unbolt the connector block from the boom and undo the nuts that hold the dipole elements. If the dipole is a folded type discard the loop and use either the directors or reflector to make up the new dipole elements. Use the aerial dimensions table given in Table 5.1 as a guide

Table 5.1 Element length guide for 1/4 and 5/8 loaded wave whips

MHz	1/4 mm	1/4 inch	5/8 mm	5/8 inch	MHz	1/4 mm	1/4 inch	5/8 mm	5/8 inch
25	2860	112.00	7150	280.0	315	226	8.91	565	22.2
30	2383	93.60	5957	234.0	320	223	8.77	557	21.9
35	2042	80.20	5105	200.0	325	220	8.64	550	21.6
40	1787	70.20	4467	175.0	330	216	8.50	540	21.2
45	1588	62.40	3970	156.0	335	213	8.38	532	20.9
50	1430	56.10	3575	140.0	340	210	8.25	525	20.6
55	1300	51.00	3250	127.0	345	207	8.13	517	20.3
60	1191	46.80	2977	117.0	350	204	8.02	510	20.0
65	1100	43.20	2750	108.0	355	201	7.90	502	19.7
70	1021	40.10	2552	100.0	360	198	7.80	495	19.5
75	953	37.40	2382	93.6	365	195	7.69	487	19.2
80	893	35.10	2232	87.7	370	193	7.58	482	18.9
85	841	33.00	2102	82.5	375	190	7.48	475	18.7
90	794	31.20	1985	78.0	380	188	7.38	470	18.4
95	752	29.50	1880	73.8	385	185	7.29	462	18.2
100	715	28.00	1787	70.2	390	183	7.20	457	18.0
105	680	26.70	1700	66.8	395	181	7.10	452	17.7
110	650	25.50	1625	63.8	400	178	7.02	445	17.5
115	621	24.40	1552	61.0	405	176	6.93	440	17.3
120	595	23.40	1487	58.5	410	174	6.84	435	17.1
125	572	22.40	1430	56.1	415	172	6.76	430	16.9
130	550	21.60	1375	54.0	420	170	6.68	425	16.7
135	529	20.80	1322	52.0	425	168	6.60	420	16.5
140	510	20.00	1275	50.1	430	166	6.53	415	16.3
145	493	19.30	1232	48.4	435	164	6.45	410	16.1
150	476	18.70	1190	46.8	440	162	6.38	405	15.9
155	461	18.10	1152	45.2	445	160	6.31	400	15.7
160	446	17.50	1115	43.8	450	158	6.24	395	15.6
165	433	17.00	1082	42.5	455	157	6.17	392	15.4
170	420	16.50	1050	41.2	460	155	6.10	387	15.2
175	408	16.00	1020	40.1	465	153	6.03	382	15.0
180	397	15.60	992	39.0	470	152	5.97	380	14.9
185	386	15.10	965	37.9	475	150	5.91	375	14.7
190	376	14.70	940	36.9	480	148	5.85	370	14.6
195	366	14.40	915	36.0	485	147	5.78	367	14.4
200	357	14.00	892	35.1	490	145	5.73	362	14.3
205	348	13.60	870	34.2	495	144	5.67	360	14.1
210	340	13.30	850	33.4	500	143	5.61	357	14.0

Table 5.1 *continued*

MHz	¼ mm	¼ inch	⅝ mm	⅝ inch	MHz	¼ mm	¼ inch	⅝ mm	⅝ inch
215	332	13.00	830	32.6	505	141	5.56	352	13.9
220	325	12.70	812	31.9	510	140	5.50	350	13.7
225	317	12.40	792	31.2	515	138	5.45	345	13.6
230	310	12.20	775	30.5	520	137	5.40	342	13.5
235	304	11.90	760	29.8	525	136	5.34	340	13.3
240	297	11.70	742	29.2	530	134	5.29	335	13.2
245	291	11.40	727	28.6	535	133	5.24	332	13.1
250	286	11.20	715	28.0	540	132	5.20	330	13.0
255	280	11.00	700	27.5	545	131	5.15	327	12.8
260	275	10.80	687	27.0	550	130	5.10	325	12.7
265	269	10.50	672	26.4	555	128	5.05	320	12.6
270	264	10.40	660	26.0	560	127	5.01	317	12.5
275	260	10.20	650	25.5	565	126	4.96	315	12.4
280	255	10.00	637	25.0	570	125	4.92	312	12.3
285	250	9.85	625	24.6	575	124	4.88	310	12.2
290	246	9.68	615	24.2	580	123	4.84	307	12.1
295	242	9.51	605	23.7	585	122	4.80	305	12.0
300	238	9.36	595	23.4	590	121	4.75	302	11.8
305	234	9.20	585	23.0	595	120	4.71	300	11.7
310	230	9.05	575	22.6	600	119	4.68	297	11.7

and, with a hacksaw, cut the two elements to the required dimensions. For general purpose listening elements of a length corresponding to a frequency 100MHz are suitable but for specific reception of such bands as marine, air, etc, just cut to the appropriate length for that frequency. Drill the cut ends and re-fit the elements to the connector block. With the rest of the elements removed, the boom can now be re-used by bolting the block to one end of the tube. All that is needed now is cable and a clamp to hold the boom to a mast.

Fitting the cable is easy — just remember to make sure that the inner core goes to the element that points upwards.

Mounting external aerials

A whole range of fittings and mounting kits is available for installing aerials and your local TV aerial erection firm should be only too happy to sell you poles, fixing kits, etc. If you are lucky, the same firm may also

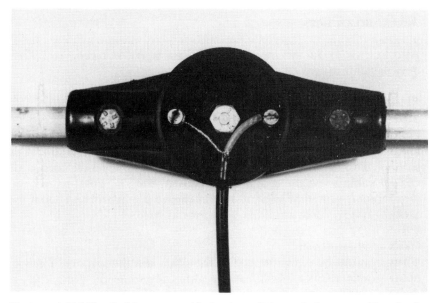

Photograph 5(g) The dipole's connector block prior to fitting to the boom arm. Note that for vertical use the element connected to the Coax cable's braid must be the one that points downwards.

have a pile of old scrap aerials and these, if they have not suffered too much from weathering, can provide a useful source of connector blocks and elements.

There are four basic ways of mounting an aerial outside and the corresponding kits are:

1 Wall mounting. This consists of a plate with brackets to hold a mounting pole. A drill capable of drilling into brick or masonry will be needed and expanding bolts should be used to retain the plate.

2 Eaves mounting. A smaller version of the wall mounting version, it is used with wood screws to fix onto the eaves. Note, though, that this method is only suitable for small lightweight aerials: even a small aerial can put considerable strain on its mountings during high winds.

3 Chimney lashing. The method often used for TV aerials, comprising one or two brackets held to a chimney by wire cable. Although easy to fit, it places the aerial in close proximity to the heat and smoke from the chimney which may accelerate the inevitable corrosion of the aerial.

4 Free standing mast. This is the most expensive solution but usually the best if you can afford it. An aluminium mast of 6 metres or more in length is partially sunk into the ground and held upright with wire guys. This mounting method can improve performance remarkably at some locations as it allows the aerial to be sited away from obstructions and above the level of trees and buildings that block signals. Planning permission may be required for this kind of installation.

Aerial amplifiers

Also known as RF or antenna amplifiers, signal boosters, etc. These devices fall into two categories:

Masthead amplifiers

These units consist of a small-signal amplifier housed in a weatherproof box, close to the aerial. They are useful for making-up for the signal losses that occur when long cables are used between the aerial and the scanner. DC current to power the unit is fed up the centre core of the coaxial cable — as the signal comes down, the DC goes up, without interference. One new variant on this theme is a broadband aerial that actually has an aerial amplifier built into its base.

Cable-end amplifiers

These connect between the end of the cable and the scanner. They are often powered by a small battery although some do plug into the domestic AC supply. Cable-end amplifiers have limitations as, unlike masthead amplifiers, they cannot improve a poor signal-to-noise ratio of an aerial system.

When to use an amplifier

In the ideal circumstances, that is, with an aerial of sufficient quality and short enough cable, an aerial amplifier is not needed. While capable of boosting weaker signals an aerial amplifier can also cause problems. For instance, strong signals received on other frequencies are also boosted and may overload the scanner.

However, some scanner users may live in areas where they are screened by high buildings or land, or may not be able to fit an aerial of sufficiently high quality. In such circumstances an amplifier *may* help. It may also be of use where long cable runs are necessary between the scanner and the aerial.

As a caution, users are advised to seek expert advice *before* installing an aerial amplifier, as wrongly doing so will cause more problems than it solves.

New and unusual aerials

Since the first edition of this book was published, two new aerials of notable interest have appeared on the market. The first is the multiband mobile antenna from Sandpiper and the other is the 'Trombone' section wide-band aerial from Butternut. Both these products are described fully in Chapter 9.

Accessories 6

Power supplies

Most non-portable scanners are supplied with a mains adaptor. Often these just consist of a small box with two leads, one going to the mains supply, the other going to the scanner. Some scanners such as the Bearcat 220FB have the circuit built-in. Whatever the scanner, the only time a scanner owner should need to buy an adaptor is perhaps if the original is lost or damaged. Some care must be taken in choosing a replacement and this warning also applies to the smaller mobile scanners and portable scanners which are not provided with an adaptor.

Some scanners have a certain amount of built-in voltage regulation and are tolerant of fairly wide DC input voltages, typically 12V to 17V. However others are more sensitive to higher voltages and damage could result if the incorrect voltage is applied.

Regulated or unregulated?

Ideally it is best to avoid unregulated supplies, in which output voltage is not stabilised and can be quite high if the current drawn by the scanner is low. Such power supplies are also more likely to cause mains hum interference. I give this warning in the knowledge that many adaptors supplied with scanners are unregulated. What must be borne in mind is that the manufacturer has usually carefully chosen the transformer so that it gives the right voltage under the load imposed by the scanner. Unless you are absolutely sure the replacement adaptor will do the same, play safe and stick to a regulated one.

Regulated supplies of 13.8V are very much standard these days and usually available for quite modest prices from scanner, amateur and CB dealers. You will need a unit capable of supplying sufficient current — for most scanners 1 amp should be more than adequate. A power supply capable of supplying higher current than the scanner requires will not harm the scanner.

Warnings

Never, under any circumstances, use a transformer designed for electric trains or cars.

Be very careful about connecting the supply polarity the right way round. Full details on this are given in Chapter 4.

Batteries

Most portable scanners are supplied with re-chargeable cells of the Ni-Cad type. Refer to Chapter 4 for specific details of charging these cells and note that you must *never* attempt to re-charge normal cells as they are likely to explode!

Ni-Cad cells have a limited lifetime (a minimum of 500 recharge cycles) and, occasionally, it may be necessary to replace them. If they are standard sizes: A, AA, C, D, etc, this presents little problem as they are now widely available, not only from radio/electrical dealers, but also from such outlets as photography shops, etc. Some scanners, though, have non-standard cells designed to fit within a certain space. Some of these can be quite difficult to obtain, particularly those used in some older models of scanner. If you are not able to obtain replacements from a scanner dealer then it is worth trying a hobby or model shop. Some cells used in radio controlled models are quite compact and can be joined together to give the required voltage. It's worth a try if you are desperate.

Loudspeakers/headphones

Loudspeakers

The loudspeaker built-in to most scanners, particularly portables, is very much of a compromise and audio output quality can usually be improved considerably by using an external loudspeaker. A larger loudspeaker than the one fitted to the scanner will often also provide louder output and this can be particularly useful in something like a noisy vehicle such as a car or lorry.

Suitable loudspeakers are available at reasonable prices from firms who stock CB equipment and chances are that such a loudspeaker will be fitted with a small jack plug which will match the socket on a lot of scanners. The loudspeaker should be of the correct impedance but this is not usually a problem as most sets will feed either 8 or 16 ohm loudspeakers and these are standard types.

I use a pair of small loudspeakers sold for use with 'Walkman' type personal cassette players. The three-pole stereo plug was removed and each lead was replaced with normal two-pole jacks. The pair of speakers were cheap, yet the 75mm units give good clear audio output quality when used with a small portable scanner.

Photograph 6(a) A small speaker designed for use with personal stereo cassette players can be fitted with a suitable plug and makes a good and inexpensive extension speaker for a scanner.

Headphones

Headphones can be attached to most scanners by plugging them into the external loudspeaker socket. They are useful where other people don't want to be disturbed by the scanner's reception.

Choice of headphones is enormous but, personally, I prefer using a pair of lightweight ones sold for use with 'Walkman' type cassette players. They are very light, very comfortable and allow you to monitor and, at the same time hear the TV, for example. This type of headphone can be bought from most radio and hi-fi dealers for just a few pounds — do not buy expensive headphones, however, as their hi-fi qualities will be wasted on a scanner. One thing you will have to do before use is to change the plug. They are invariably fitted with a miniature three-pole jack plug and a two-pole plug is standard for connection to scanners. The lead into the headphone's jack plug will probably consist of two coaxial cables. The screens from both of these should be twisted together and soldered to the body (sleeve) connector of the replacement jack plug. The two inner cores should also be joined together and then soldered to the centre (tip) connector of the plug. Make sure that no short circuits between tip and body occur. This type of connection is called 'parallel' and, because these mini-headphones all are of high impedance, this method of connection will not harm the scanner. Other types of headphones, of low impedance, may damage the scanner if connected this way, however. Although the lightweight headphones

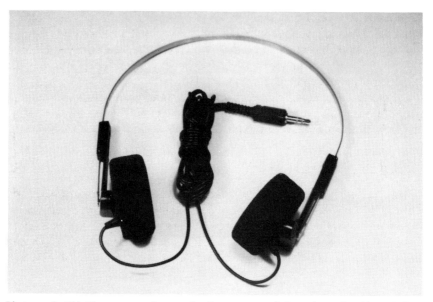

Photograph 6(b) Cheap personal stereo headsets are very light and comfortable and allow scanner listening without disturbing others. The three pole plug will have to be changed for a two pole miniature jack.

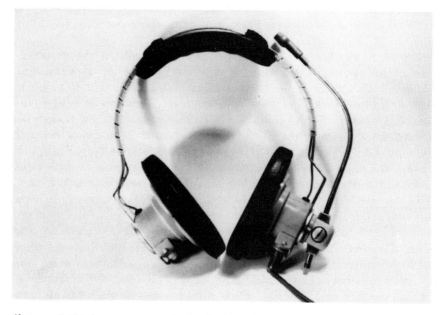

Photograph 6(c) A proper communication headset. These Airlite-62's are available for a few pounds from many government surplus dealers and once cleaned-up are ideal for scanner use. The microphone boom can easily be removed if not required.

mentioned here can be worn for hours without discomfort they do not exclude external noise. If noise exclusion is needed then heavier headphones of the type with ear muffs will have to be used. Again, the types stocked by hi-fi shops will do the job or you can get purpose made communication types from specialist dealers.

When buying any kind of headphone try them on in the shop. Some people find certain types of headphones very uncomfortable and they are very much a matter of personal choice.

Computer interfacing

In several chapters of this book reference has been made to connecting a scanner to a computer in order to interpret or decode certain types of transmission. Quite a large selection of computer software exists to do tasks like these for most of the major home computers, typically the Commodore 64 & VIC-20, BBC, Sinclair Spectrum & ZX-81, Dragon 32 & 64, Acorn Electron and some Amstrad models.

Interfaces

In most instances it is not possible to connect the audio output of the scanner straight into the computer. Under these circumstances it is necessary to use an interface. Interfaces vary in complexity from single transistor circuits to highly complex units capable of breaking down such things as transmitted satellite weather pictures into a digital form a computer can deal with.

On the other hand, there are cases where it *is* possible to connect the scanner directly to the computer. A typical example is the radioteletype (RTTY) program for my own Dragon 64 computer. Here the output from the scanner's loudspeaker socket is connected directly to the computer's cassette input port. Similar set-ups are available for other computers. This kind of arrangement, unfortunately only works with a strong clear signal. One of the advantages of using a proper interface is that it contains circuits to remove interference, cope with fading signals and so forth.

Let us now take a detailed look at the kind of software needed to decode various signals and the interfaces needed.

Morse code (CW)

Morse code decoding programs are available for most home computers including the unexpanded ZX-81. Software available for Sinclair computers generally needs no interface. Other computers may need a simple single transistor tone decoder. Unfortunately there appears to be few of these decoders available as ready made units. Scarab Systems, however, can supply a simple unit for most home computers.

It is worth noting that most of the more complex RTTY decoders also work extremely well as CW decoders. The scanner, however, must have a BFO circuit and be capable of receiving CW.

Radioteletype (RTTY)

Often nicknamed the 'long distance typewriter' at VHF/UHF frequencies, RTTY transmissions are mostly found on amateur bands. Again, software and a computer can be used to print out the received and decoded transmissions. Most RTTY traffic is transmitted as an SSB signal which can only be decoded if the scanner has suitable BFO circuitry. Some RTTY, though, is transmitted as dual-tone FM and to a lesser extent as AM. Software is available for a wide range of computers but in many cases a suitable decoder will be required and these are quite expensive.

Slow scan television (SSTV)

SSTV is a specialised type of transmission and is really only used to any great extent by amateurs. This means that the range of software available to decode SSTV transmissions for computer use is restricted but does exist. Some computers, such as the Sinclair Spectrum can be programmed with software that requires no interface. Most computers, however, require some kind of interface. Some RTTY decoders can also successfully be used to decode SSTV transmissions.

The quality of picture received depends largely on the screen resolution of the computer. Some older models only give a very coarse image but others such as the BBC and Commodore 64 provide excellent reproduction possibilities. With the right software, the received image may be dumped to a printer.

SSTV activity is found on the amateur VHF 2 metre band and the UHF 70 cm band. Look at the data in Chapter 7 for details. Unlike CW and RTTY, SSTV does not need a BFO circuit and can be received on any scanner capable of covering the bands. It can be recognised as a buzzing noise interspersed with blips of tone.

During 1985, amateurs around the world were thrilled to see SSTV pictures sent from the American space shuttle. On board the shuttle was an astronaut who holds an amateur radio licence and he was able to send back still pictures from several of the on-board cameras. I received pictures myself, using a Bearcat 220FB attached to a simple whip aerial in the garden. I recorded the tones that made up the pictures on an ordinary cassette recorder, later playing them back, via an interface, into a computer.

Availabilty of software

Table 6.1 is a list of available software which has been compiled from advertisements appearing in UK amateur radio magazines at the time of

Table 6.1 Available computer software to decode specialised transmissions

Computer	CW	RTTY	SSTV	Multi
Spectrum	●	●	●	●
Commodore 64	●	●	●	●
VIC 20	●	●	●	●
Commodore 4/16/28	●	●		
BBC-B	●	●	●	●
Dragon 32/64	●	●		●
Amstrad CPC 464	●	●	●	
Atari 6/800XL	●			
Pet		●		
Commodore Amiga			●	

writing. A copy of any of the major magazines will enable a scanner user to find suitable software for an attached computer.

Multi means single programs able to cope with a variety of transmission types. Software is available in a variety of mediums including: cassette tape, disc, Sinclair Microdrive, plug-in cartridge and EPROM chip (BBC-B)

For details of suitable interface terminals see the equipment review on accessories in Chapter 9.

Weather pictures

Weather picture decoding is yet another application for computers hooked up to a scanner. So far, though, the only commercially available systems are for the BBC-B. Maplin, Halbar and Cirkit produce software.

Weather pictures are sent in a similar way to slow scan television in that the satellite's camera pictures are encoded into tones. These not only represent the various shades that make up the picture but also such things as synchronising pulses. For weather satellite transmission reception, the scanner must have a minimum of 30kHz bandwidth in FM mode (WFM). Scanners such as the AOR's, Regency MX series, Yaesu and Icom are all capable of this.

Software for the BBC-B is on sideways-ROM or on disc.

The systems are designed to work primarily with NOAAs 11 and 10 satellites. These are polar orbiting satellites which make passes at about every 102 minutes, during which time the earth will turn through 25.5 degrees. The signals can be recorded on an ordinary cassette tape

Figure 6.1 A screen dump using the Computer Concepts 'Printmaster' ROM.

recorder and the Timestep interface has a circuit which will switch on the recorder when it detects a satellite signal. In this way it is possible to leave the equipment alone and then play back the pictures later. These can be shown on the monitor screen or dumped to a dot-matrix printer (see Figure 6.1).

Facilities are available on some interfaces to decode signals from other satellites, notably those of Russian origin and some can even be configured for normal slow scan television.

Frequencies of various satellite transmissions are given in Chapter 7.

Frequency converters

These devices extend the coverage of scanners (or indeed any VHF receiver). The system designed for use with the SX-400 scanner is rather specialised and that is covered in more detail below. The other converters on the market are designed to provide VHF/UHF scanners with coverage of the lower HF bands. They fall into two categories; external stand-alone circuitry and internally fitted.

The simplest of these devices are manufactured by Datong, Kuranishi and AKD. They simply plug into the scanner's antenna socket and then HF coverage is provided when the scanner is tuned to certain frequencies. In the case of the Datong converter, the scanner is tuned to the amateur 2 Metre band and HF coverage is tuned on the converter itself. The AKD device has no external controls. Tuning the scanner between 100.1MHz and 60MHz provides coverage between 100kHz and 60MHz.

Several UK scanner supplies offer specially modified versions of scanners, notably the FRG-9600 and Icom R7000, which have similar adaptors built into them and these are switched into circuit by a switch on either the front or back panel.

SX-400 system

The only other available frequency converters are the dedicated SX-400 modules. They are designed to work with the JIL SX-400 scanner. There are two down-converters, the RF-8014 and the RF5080. The RF-8014 extends SX-400 coverage from 800 to 1400MHz; the RF5080 from 500 to 800MHz. When in use with the SX-400, the scanner sends a control signal to the converter, switching it into or out of circuit.

JIL also offers an up-converter for the SX-400 which operates in the same way. In this case, though, the converter covers the entire LF/MF/HF spectrum from 100kHz to 30MHz. This module also has extra facilities such as allowing reception of SSB and CW transmissions.

These converters will also work with some other scanners but will not automatically switch in and out of circuit.

Specifications of all converters are given in Chapter 9.

Miscellaneous

Aerial switch

There may be occasions when a scanner user needs to change aerials connected to the scanner. For instance, although a discone is suitable for reception of most transmissions, if the user wishes to receive satellite transmissions a crossed dipole is required. Obviously it is of no great hardship to unplug one aerial and plug in the other, but a neater solution is an aerial switch. These usually consist of a small box with a switch of rotary, toggle or push button type. In use the two aerial connections form inputs to the switch box and the output, after switching is fed to the scanner. They vary greatly in quality and some of the cheaper types, particularly those sold as CB accessories, may have enormous losses at VHF/UHF frequencies. If you wish to use an aerial switch, make sure it is of the right type to match your scanner and aerial systems.

Slide mount bracket

One problem with using a scanner in a vehicle is that the equipment is at the mercy of thieves. One answer to this is to use a quick-release slide mounting bracket which allows the scanner to be easily removed — by the owner! They are widely available form CB radio dealers and consist of two parts: a holder and a sliding carrier. The holder is fitted with contacts that match up to contacts on the sliding section. The contacts are used to allow plug-in connections for power supply and external loudspeaker purposes, to and from the scanner.

Some users also use contacts for the aerial feed but this is not a good idea as the type of contacts used are not suited to low-level radio signals.

Installation of a slide mount bracket is fairly straightforward, but a soldering iron will be needed to make connections to the contacts. The scanner itself is bolted to the slide carrier. The holder is located in a suitable position; fixed with either self-tapping screws or small nuts and bolts.

In use, the sliding carrier complete with scanner is quickly removed, and while the owner is away from the vehicle, can be stored, say, in the boot, where it is out of temptation's way.

UK frequency allocations 7

The decision on who transmits what, on which frequency, is made by international agreement. Clearly, governments must agree on allocations if they are to avoid causing interference. There would be chaos if, say, one country allocated a band to low powered radio telephones while a neighbouring country allocated the same brand for high powered broadcasting. The body which co-ordinates radio frequency allocations on behalf of world governments is the International Telecommunications Union, known simply as the ITU.

For the purpose of agreed allocations the ITU splits the world into three regions. The United Kingdom falls in Region 1, which includes most of Europe and a small section of North Africa. However, it does not necessarily follow that each country conforms strictly with the allocations drawn up for that region. Where there is little likelihood of interference, countries may opt for local variations and, obviously, many such variations exist. For this reason, listings given in this book strictly apply only to the United Kingdom, although most allocations do match the standard format for Region 1.

We shall look first at general VHF/UHF frequency allocations, then consider in detail some of the services on those allocations. Table 7.1/2 is a listing of UK frequency allocations.

Table 7.1/2 UK VHF frequency allocations

From-to Pairing	Allocation
25.0050–25.0100	Standard Frequency, time signals, space research
25.0100–25.0700	Fixed (PTO & Government), Maritime & Land Mobile (Government)
25.0700–25.1100	Maritime Mobile (mostly CW)

Table 7.1/2   *continued*

From-to	Pairing	Allocation
25.0539	26.1444	Ship-to-shore (SSB)
25.0601	26.1506	Ship-to-shore (SSB)
25.0710		Marine Calling channel 'A' (CW)
25.0730		Marine Calling channel 'B' (CW)
25.0750		Marine Calling channel 'C' (CW)
25.0763 to 25.0898		Marine channels spaced 0.5KHz (CW)
25.1100–25.6000		Fixed (PTO & Government), Maritime & Land Mobile (government)
25.1100 to 25.5350		World-wide coastal stations (mostly CW but some SSB)
25.5500 to 25.6000		As above plus Radio Astronomy
25.6000–26.1000		Broadcasting (AM) plus Radio Astronomy
26.1000–27.5000		Fixed (PTO & Government), Land Mobile (including CEPT CB system), pagers, ISM, Maritime Mobile, model control
26.1444	25.0539	Shore-to-ship (SSB)
26.1506	25.0601	Shore-to-ship (SSB)
26.2375 to 26.8655		One-way paging systems (new band)
26.9780 to 27.2620		One-way paging systems (old band)

Table 7.1/2   *continued*

From-to	Pairing	Allocation
26.9570 to 27.2830		Industrial, scientific and medical
26.9600 to 27.2800		Model control (AM & FM & 1.5Watt maximum power) & Data Buoys
26.9650 to 27.4050		CEPT Citizens Band radio (mostly NFM but some illegal AM & SSB)
27.4500		Emergency alarm systems for the elderly or infirmed
27.5000–27.6000		Land Mobile (government) Meteorological aids (Sondes, etc)
27.6000–28.0000		Land Mobile (UK CB system) & Meteorological Aids
27.6010 to 27.9910		UK Citizens Band radio system (NFM)
28.0000–29.7000		Amateur Radio (10Metre Band) including USSR RS-series satellites
29.7000–30.7000		Space (satellite identification), Mobile (Government) & Fixed
29.7000 to 29.9700		Military 25KHz channel spacing simplex communications
29.7000 to 30.0100		Satellite identification

Table 7.1/2   *continued*

From-to	Pairing	Allocation
30.0250 to 31.7000		USAF (Europe) mobile communications
30.4500		US Military 'MARS' radio integration network
30.700–34.5000		Fixed, Mobile & Paging systems (at the peak of 11 year sunspot cycles many US services operating in this band can be heard)
30.7000 to 34.5000		Many channels in use by USAF in UK/Europe
31.7250		Hospital paging systems
31.7500		Hospital paging systems
31.7750		Hospital paging systems
31.8000 to 34.9000		Military Fixed/Mobile 50KHz channel spacing
34.5000–37.5000		Mobile (mostly government & military), Model Control, Alarms
34.9250		Emergency alarm systems for the elderly or infirmed
34.9500		Emergency alarm systems for the elderly or infirmed
34.9750		Emergency alarm systems for the elderly or infirmed
35.0050 to 35.2050		Model Control (aircraft only) 1.5Watt maximum power
35.2500 to 37.7500		Military Fixed/Mobile 50KHz channel spacing

Table 7.1/2   *continued*

From-to	Pairing	Allocation
37.5000–47.0000		Mobile (extensively military vehicles and manpacks), Radio Astronomy, ISM, cordless telephones & Television broadcasting
37.7500 to 38.2500		Cambridge Observatory (astronomy)
37.7500 to 40.0000		Military mobile 50KHz channel spacing
39.9150 to 40.1200		Some beacons on space satellites have used this sub-band
40.0500 40.6800		★★★Military Distress Frequency★★★ Industrial, Scientific & Medical
41.0000 to 46.0000		Military tactical mobile (vehicles/manpacks) 50KHz channel spacing
41.0000 to 68.0000		Television Broadcasting (not UK) band 1
46.6100 to 46.9700		Unapproved cordless telephone handsets (US system B - NFM)
47.45625 to 45.54375		Cordless telephone handsets (approved - 8 Channels NFM)
47.6800–50.0000		Land Mobile, Broadcasting, Amateur & unapproved baby listeners, walkie-talkies, wireless microphones & cordless 'phones (all NFM)

Table 7.1/2   *continued*

From-to	Pairing	Allocation
48.9900 to 49.6800	69.7200 to 70.2750	Unapproved long range cordless phone bases (22 Channels NFM)
49.0000 to 49.8750		Private paging systems
49.0000 to 50.0000		Unapproved devices listed above mostly intended for use in USA
49.4250 to 49.4750		Hospital paging systems
49.6700 to 49.9700		Unapproved cordless telephone bases (US system B NFM)
49.8200 to 49.9000		Low powered radio control toys, baby alarms, etc (100MW max power)
49.8300 to 49.8900		Unapproved cordless telephones
50.0000-54.0000		6 Metre Amateur band (US allocation - NFM, CW & SSB)
50.0000 to 52.0000		6 Metre Amateur band (UK allocation - NFM, CW & SSB)
54.0000		Frequency has been used by space satellite beacons (Anna-1B)

Table 7.1/2   *continued*

From-to	Pairing	Allocation
52.0000–60.0000		Land Mobile and radio microphones
53.8000 to 55.6000		BBC high powered radio microphones
60.0000–64.0000		Radio Microphones
60.8000 to 62.6000		BBC high powered radio microphones
64.0000–68.0000		Fixed & Land Mobile including Military
68.0000–70.0250		Land Mobile & Repeaters (military)
69.3000		Spot frequency for Sea Cadets (AM)
69.6000 to 69.8000	84.6000 to 84.8000	Military repeater outputs
69.8250 to 69.9750		Outside Broadcast camera links
70.0000 to 70.0500		Unapproved cordless 'phones
70.0250–70.5000		4Metre Amateur Band. CW, NFM and SSB in use
70.5000–71.5000		Land Mobile (emergency services)
70.5000 to 71.5000	80.0000 to 84.0000	Fire service bases

Table 7.1/2   *continued*

From-to	Pairing	Allocation
71.5000–72.8000		LOW BAND PMR mobiles (bases + 13.5MHz)
71.5125 to 72.7875	85.0125 to 86.2875	Extensively used by Water Boards, Telecoms & Local Authorities using both AM and NFM
72.0000 to 72.0625	85.5000 to 85.5625	Extensively used by the Automobile Association (callsign 'Fanum')
72.3750	85.8750	Short-term hire mobile
72.5250 to 72.7000	86.0250 to 86.2000	Ambulance bases in some areas
72.5375	86.0375	Private Ambulances National Network (Mobiles)
72.8000–74.8000		Land mobile (Government)
72.8000 to 73.7000		Military simplex channels using 25KHz spacing
73.7000 to 73.9250		Military (RAF ground services) & MOULD repeater inputs
74.8000–75.2000		Aeronavigation guard band
75.0000		Approach fan beams, inner, middle & outer markers (AM)
75.2000–76.7000		Outside broadcast links and military - mostly allocated to USAF British bases (NFM) and MOULD repeater outputs

Table 7.1/2 *continued*

From-to	Pairing	Allocation
75.20000 to 75.30000		BBC outside broadcast links
75.75000 to 76.50000		Military MOULD repeater outputs
76.7000–78.0000		Fixed and Land mobile (PMR and government)
76.9625 to 77.5000	86.9625 to 87.5000	Fixed and Mobile. Government, Customs, British Telecom and PMR mobiles
78.0000–80.0000		Land Mobile. Government and private users.
78.1000		Air Training Corps (nationwide)
78.1900		BBC OB and engineering (channel 1)
78.2155		BBC OB and engineering (channel 3)
78.2250		Microwave link setting-up channel (nationwide) and BBC OB crews (channel 2)
78.2275		BBC OB and engineering (channel 4)
78.2525		BBC OB and engineering (channel 6)
78.2400		BBC OB and engineering (channel 5)
79.0000 to 80.0000		MOULD repeater inputs and RAF ground services
80.0000–84.0000		Land Mobiles & Fixed (extensive emergency service use). Allocations which couple with Band II (97.6 - 102.1) will move from here by 1994.
80.5000 to 82.5000		Radio Astronomy (Cambridge University)

Table 7.1/2   *continued*

From-to	Pairing	Allocation
80.0000 to 84.0000	70.5000 to 71.5000	**Fire Mobiles**
83.9960 to 84.0040		**ISM**
84.0000–85.0000		Fixed & Land Mobile (mostly military)
84.1250 to 84.3500	73.7000 to 73.9250	**RAF ground service bases**
84.3000		**RAF Mountain rescue teams (single frequency simplex)**
84.0000 to 85.0000		**Military repeater inputs**
85.0000–88.0000		**LOW BAND PMR Bases**
85.0125 to 86.2875	71.5125 to 72.7825	Extensively used by Water Boards, Telecoms, Local Authorities & Community Repeaters using both AM and FM
85.1375 to 85.2000		**Numerous British Telecom engineering channels**
85.4875 to 85.5625	71.9875 to 72.0625	**Automobile Association 'Fanum' bases**
85.8500	72.2500	Pye Telecom National engineering channel
85.8750	72.3750	Low Band demonstration and short term hire channel bases
86.0375	72.5375	Private Ambulance bases National Network

Table 7.1/2   *continued*

From-to	Pairing	Allocation
86.1375	72.6375	Storno Telecom national engineering channel
86.2000	72.7000	Automobile Association 'Fanum'
86.3000 to 86.3500		Single Frequency Simplex channels (channels listed below are in use in many parts of Britain but may vary in some areas)
86.3125		National Mountain Rescue channel 1
86.3250		St John Ambulance/Red Cross Channel 1
86.3500		National Mountain Rescue channel 2 (in some areas, Red Cross, St John Ambulance, REACT and lifeguards)
86.3625		Scouts national channel 1
86.3750		REACT CB emergency teams (nationwide)
86.4125		St John Ambulance/Red Cross Channel 2
86.4250		Forestry Commission channel 3
86.4375		Motor Rally Safety Channel
86.4500		Forestry Commission channel 2
86.4625		County Councils
86.4750		British Rail National Incident Channel
86.5000		Nuclear Spills Teams Channel 1
86.5250		Nuclear Spills Teams Channel 2
86.5500		Nuclear Spills Teams Channel 3
86.5750		NCB mine rescue teams
86.6250		Scouts national channel 2
86.6750		Nuclear fire and radiation check teams
86.7000		BNF nuclear hazard check teams
86.9625 to 87.5000	76.9625 to 77.5000	Split Frequency Simplex bases
87.0000 to 87.0500		RAC services
87.1625 to 87.6250		Numerous County Council Highways Departments

Table 7.1/2   *continued*

From-to	Pairing	Allocation
87.7625	77.7625	Forestry Commission National channel 2
87.8250	77.8250	Forestry Commission National channel 1
87.9250	77.9250	Newspapers & Racing result services
87.9625	77.9625	Forestry Commission National Channel 3
88.0000–108.0000		Broadcasting & Land Mobile (until 1994). This allocation includes the UK FM Broadcast Band (Band 11).
97.6000 to 102.1000		Emergency Service Bases with mobiles at 80-84MHz. AM & NFM used.
99.0230		Frequency has been used by Russian Satellites (Cosmos 44)
105.0000 to 108.0000	138.0000 to 141.0000	PMR Mobiles (transport services)
105.35625	138.35625	British Rail
108.0000–117.9750		Aeronautical Radionavigation beacons including VHF Omnirange (VOR) and Doppler VOR (DVOR). Beacons identified by a three letter code in CW. Some of those located at or near airfields carry AM voice information on weather/runway/warnings etc. This service is known as Aerodrome Terminal Information Service (ATIS)
118.0500–135.9750		International Aeronautical Mobile Band. This is the VHF band used by all civilian and some military airfields. It is subdivided into 720 channels (25KHz spacing) and mode is AM
118.0000 to 123.0000		Mostly control tower frequencies

Table 7.1/2   *continued*

From-to	Pairing	Allocation
121.5000		★★★International Distress Frequency★★★
121.7500		Soyuz manned T-flights to MIR Space Station (non-standard use of this allocation using NFM)
123.0000 to 130.0000		Mostly airways frequencies (some ground & approach control)
123.1000		Search & Rescue (SAR)
130.0000 to 132.0000		Mostly company frequencies (airline crews to ground staff)
132.0000 to 136.0000		Mostly airways
135.5500 to 135.6450		Sub-band was once used for the American ATS series satellites
136.0000-138.0000		Space to Earth Communications & Weather Imaging Satellites (see satellite sub-section for full details)
138.0000-141.0000		Land Mobile PMR (extensive use by Gas and Electricity Boards). Paired with bases at -33MHz in Band 11 due to end in 1995
138.00625 to 140.89375	105.00625 to 107.89375	PMR bases
138.0750 to 138.1750		Mercury and Racal Paging Systems

Table 7.1/2   *continued*

From-to	Pairing	Allocation
138.0000 to 138.2000		USAF bases in some areas
138.35625	105.35625	British Rail
138.5000 to 139.50000		Mostly Gas Boards
139.50000 to 140.5000	148.0000 to 149.0000	Mostly Electricity Boards (new allocation)
140.1825		Central Electricity Generating Board national line fault teams
140.1875		Central Electricity Generating Board national line fault teams
140.2000		Central Electricity Generating Board national line fault teams
140.5000 to 141.0000		Bus companies
140.96875		Short-term hire channel (single frequency simplex)
141.0000–141.9000		Land Mobile mostly used by BBC, Independent Television and Radio for outside broadcast links, radio cars, etc. All Single Frequency Simplex using NFM.
141.0000 to 141.2000		Mostly ITV

Table 7.1/2   *continued*

From-to	Pairing	Allocation
141.2000 to 141.9000		141 Mostly BBC
141.9000–143.0000		Mobile (Government) including land, air & space satellite communications & Military MOULD repeater links (NFM)
142.0000 to 143.0000		Air-to-Air and Air-to-Ground. Sub-band used fairly extensively by military in continental Europe but rarely in UK
142.4000 to 142.6000		Extensively used for Soyuz/Mir (USSR) satellite links (NFM)
142.7200		**USAF Air-to-Air**
142.8200		**USAF Air-to-Air**
143.0000–144.0000		Mobile (government) mobiles (largely AM) coupled with bases at + 9MHz. Some USSR space satellite traffic all using NFM.
143.1450 to 143.6250		Soyuz/Mir communications
143.6250		Mir main downlink over Europe (very strong when overhead)
144.0000–146.0000		Amateur 2Metre Band including satellite allocations. CW, SSB & NFM used
146.0000–148.0000		Land Mobile & Fixed. Emergency service mobile channels paired with bases on 154-156MHz

Table 7.1/2   *continued*

From-to	Pairing	Allocation
146.0000 to 148.0000		Emergency service Fixed links (base to hilltop)
146.0000 to 148.0000	154.0000 to 156.0000	Emergency service mobiles
147.8000		Used in many areas for Fire Brigade alert pagers
148.0000-149.0000		Fixed and Land Mobile. Gas and Electricity Boards paired with mobiles on 138.5-140.5MHz. Satellite uplinks
148.56000		NOAA-series satellite telecommand uplink
149.0000-149.9000		Mobile (Military). Used particularly by USAF and RAF and MOULD repeaters
149.8500		Common channel at many military bases
149.9000		Air Training Corps nationwide (channel 2)
149.9000-150.0500		Radionavigation by satellite. Doppler shift position fixing using US satellites (TRANSIT) and USSR (COSNAV) paired with 399.9-400.05MHz
150.0500-152.0000		Radio Astronomy and Oil Slick Markers
150.1100 to 150.1850		Slick Markers
152.0000-153.0000		Land Mobile (emergency services) bases paired with mobiles at 143-144MHz
153.0000-153.5000		National and local area radio paging systems

Table 7.1/2   *continued*

From-to	Pairing	Allocation
153.5000-154.0000		Land Mobile (Government) and meteorological aids
154.0000-156.0000		Fixed and Mobile (Emergency services). This band is used extensively for downlinks from hill-top repeaters to base stations.
154.0000 to 156.0000	146.0000 to 148.0000	Emergency Bases
156.0000-174.0000		Fixed & Mobile (land and Marine). The Marine VHF service falls within this band which also includes message handling services and mobile telephone systems. All NFM.
156.0000		Marine channel '0'. Lifeboats and Coastguard
156.0000 to 157.4250		Marine channels single and split frequency Simplex
156.8000		★★★Marine Distress & Calling channel 16★★★
157.4500 to 158.4000		Private Marine channels & message handling services
158.4000 to 158.5250		Private and Dockside using Simplex
158.5250 to 159.9125	163.0375 to 164.4250	B.T. Radiophone mobiles

Table 7.1/2   *continued*

From-to	Pairing	Allocation
159.2500 to 160.5500		Private channels and message handling services
160.5500 to 161.0000		Marine Channels
161.0000 to 161.1000	459.1000 to 459.5000	Paging systems acknowledge
161.1250 to 161.5000		Private Marine channels
161.5000 to 162.0500		Marine channels
162.0500 to 163.0000		Private channels and message handling services
163.0375 to 164.4250	158.5125 to 159.9125	B.T. Radiophone bases
164.4375 to 165.0375		Private message handling services including paging and telephone patching
165.0625 to 168.2500	169.8625 to 173.0500	HIGH BAND PMR bases. Also extensive use by security/message handling services including nationwide links
166.0000		Soyuz/Mir (USSR) satellite downlinks

Table 7.1/2 *continued*

From-to	Pairing	Allocation
166.2750 to 166.5250		Extensively used by ambulances
166.6375 167.2000	172.2000	Rediffusion engineers in some areas HIGH BAND demonstration & short term hire channel bases
167.9920 to 168.0080		Industrial, scientific & Medical
168.31215 to 168.8375		Emergency service Fixed Links
168.9500 to 169.8500		HIGH BAND PMR Simplex channels
169.0125 to 169.7625		Short term hire channels (single frequency simplex) all NFM (used extensively during the RAC Rally)
168.9750		BBC Engineering
169.8625 to 173.0500	165.0625 to 168.2500	PMR mobiles. Extensively used by security/message handling services including nationwide links
172.0000	167.2000	Short term hire mobiles
170.4500 to 170.8000	165.8500 to 166.0000	Private Security Firms mobiles
173.0500 to 173.2000		Low powered devices

Table 7.1/2 *continued*

From-to	Pairing	Allocation
173.2000 to 173.3500		Low Powered telemetry and telecontrol
173.3500 to 173.8000		Radio deaf aids, Medical and biological telemetry
173.8000 to 175.0000		Radiomicrophones
174.5000–225.0000		Land Mobile, Fixed, Radiolocation & Radiomicrophones, Television Broadcasting (not UK) Band III. Upwards from 174MHz falls within the old Band III TV allocation and these frequencies have only been released for Land Mobile in recent years. Activity may be low in some areas but should increase in time. Some shared services operate on a 'Trunked' system where the mobile is automatically switched from one base station to another as in Cellular Radio
174.0000 to 174.5000		Emergency service fixed links
174.5000 to 176.5000		PMR Simplex channels & Radiomicrophones
176.5000 to 183.5000	184.5000 to 191.5000	PMR bases

Table 7.1/2   *continued*

From-to	Pairing	Allocation
183.5000 to 184.5000		PMR Simplex channels
184.5000 to 191.5000	176.5000 to 183.5000	PMR mobiles
191.5000 to 192.5000		PMR Simplex channels
192.5000 to 199.5000	200.5000 to 207.5000	PMR (Transport Industries) mobiles and trunked networks
199.5000 to 200.5000		PMR Simplex channels
200.5000 to 207.5000	192.5000 to 199.5000	PMR (Transport Industries) bases and trunked networks
207.5000 to 208.5000		PMR Simplex channels
208.5000 to 215.5000	216.5000 to 223.5000	PMR bases
215.5000 to 216.5000		PMR Simplex channels
216.5000 to 223.5000	208.5000 to 215.5000	PMR mobiles

Table 7.1/2   *continued*

From-to	Pairing	Allocation
223.5000 to 225.0000		PMR Simplex channels
225.0000–328.6000		Aeronautical mobile (military) using AM simplex, ground-to-air, air-to-air, tactical, etc. Some satellite allocations.
235.0000 to 273.0000		Extensively used for military satellite downlinks (FleetSatcom West etc)
243.0000		★★★Military distress frequency★★★ Life-raft beacons, SARBE's, EPIRBs, etc. Frequency monitored by COSPAS/SARSAT satellites
257.8000 259.7000 296.8000		Common airfield frequency NASA Shuttles (AM voice) NASA Shuttles (AM voice particularly used on 'spacewalks')
326.5000 to 328.5000		Radio astronomy (Jodrell Bank)
344.0000 362.3000		Common airfield frequency Common airfield frequency
328.6000–335.4000		Aeronautical radionavigation — ILS glideslope beams paired with VORs in the 108-118MHz band.
335.4000–399.9000		Aeronautical mobile (military) using AM simplex, ground-to-air, air-to-air, tactical, etc.
360.0440 to 361.4400		Band has been used by US ATS-series satellites

Table 7.1/2   *continued*

From-to	Pairing	Allocation
399.9000–400.0500		Radionavigation by satellite. Doppler shift position fixing using US satellites (TRANSIT) and USSR (COSNAV) paired with 149.9-150.05MHz band
400.0000–400.1500		Standard frequency and time signal satellites
401.0000–406.0000		Fixed and mobile, meteorological satellites, space-earth communications
401.0000 to 402.0000		Space-Earth communications
401.0000 to 403.0000		Meteorological sondes & satellites
401.0000 to 405.0000		Military telemetry links
406.0000–406.1000		Mobile satellite space-earth communications
406.05000		Emergency locator beacons (identification and location by satellite)
406.1000–410.0000		Fixed and mobile (Government), radio astronomy & radio positioning aids
406.5000 to 409.0000		North Sea oil rig positioning aids
410.0000–420.0000		Fixed & mobile (Government). Extensively used by USAF using 25KHz channeling, Simplex

Table 7.1/2   *continued*

From-to	Pairing	Allocation
412.0500		Frequency has been used by US ATS-series satellites
420.0000–450.0000		Fixed, Mobile, Amateur & radiolocation
420.0000 to 422.0000		Military MOULD links
422.0000 to 425.0000		Military & Radio altimeters
425.0250 to 425.4750	445.5250 to 445.9750	PMR mobiles
425.5250 to 428.9750	440.0250 to 443.4750	PMR bases
429.0000 to 431.0000		Military & Radiolocation
431.00625 to 431.99375	448.00625 to 448.99375	PMR mobiles (London only)
432.0000 to 440.0000		70CM Amateur Band & Military (Syledis radiolocation system and MOULD links). SSB, NFM, CW, slow and fast scan TV, RTTY, Amtor, etc
440.0250 to 443.4750	425.5250 to 428.9750	PMR bases. Many transport system users (taxis, buses, etc.)

Table 7.1/2   *continued*

From-to	Pairing	Allocation
443.5000 to 445.5000		Military & radiolocation
445.5250 to 445.9750	425.0250 to 425.4750	PMR bases
446.0250 to 446.4750		PMR simplex (extensively used for Outside Broadcast links)
448.00625 to 448.99375	431.00625 to 431.99375	PMR Bases (London area only)
449.7500 to 450.0000		Earth-Space Telecommand
450.0000–470.0000		Fixed & Mobile (including marine). Mostly PMR with some emergency services, Paging, telemetry, etc.
450.0000 to 451.0000	464.0000 to 465.0000	B.T. Fixed links
451.0000 to 453.0000	464.9000 to 467.0000	Extensively used for emergency service bases and fixed links
453.0250 to 453.9750	459.5250 to 460.4750	PMR Bases
454.0125 to 454.8250		Wide area paging systems

Table 7.1/2   *continued*

From-to	Pairing	Allocation
455.0000 to 455.5000		BBC, ITV, ILR Base units for O.B's (some units paired with mobiles at + 5.5MHz).
455.5000 to 456.0000		Some PMR (Scotland) & airport ground services
456.0000 to 456.9750	461.50000 to 462.4750	PMR Bases (extensively used at airports)
456.9250	462.4250	Short-term hire bases
457.0000 to 457.5000	462.5000 to 463.0000	Point-to-point links (fixed)
457.50625 to 458.49375	463.00625 to 463.99375	Scanning telemetry
457.5250	467.5250	On-board-ship communications (international)
457.5500	467.5500	On-board-ship communications (international)
457.5750	467.5750	On-board-ship communications (international)
457.5250	467.7500	On-board-ship communications (US/Canada system)
457.5500	467.7750	On-board-ship communications (US/Canada system)
457.5750	467.8000	On-board-ship communications (US/Canada system)
457.6000	467.8250	On-board-ship communications (US/Canada system)

Table 7.1/2   *continued*

From-to	Pairing	Allocation
458.5000 to 459.5000		Model control, paging, telemetry & local communications
458.5000 to 458.8000		Low power (1/2Watt) telemetry
459.1000 to 459.5000	161.0000 to 161.0000	On-site paging systems (VHF channels are return 'acknowledge' signal)
459.5250 to 460.4750	453.0250 to 453.9750	PMR Mobiles
460.5000 to 461.5000	467.0000 to 468.0000	Point-to-point links & some airport ground services, Broadcast engineering, etc.
461.5000 to 462.4750	456.0000 to 456.9750	PMR Mobiles
462.4250 462.4750	456.9250	Short-term hire channel mobiles Long-term hire (single frequency simplex)
462.5000 to 463.0000	457.5000 to 458.5000	Point-to-Point links (fixed)
464.0000		Spot frequency has been used by some US & French satellites
464.0000 to 465.0000	450.0000 to 457.0000	B.T. Fixed links

Table 7.1/2   *continued*

From-to	Pairing	Allocation
465.0000 to 467.0000	451.0000 to 453.0000	Emergency service mobiles and fixed links
466.0000		Spot frequency has been used by some Soviet Ocean reconnaissance satellites.
467.0000 to 467.8250		Point-to-point links & ILR broadcast links using simplex & On-board-ship communications
467.5250	457.5250	On-board-ship communications (international)
467.5500	457.5500	On-board-ship communications (international)
467.5750	457.5750	On-board-ship communications (international)
467.7500	457.5250	On-board-ship communications (US/Canada system)
467.7750	457.5500	On-board-ship communications (US/Canada system)
467.8000	457.5750	On-board-ship communications (US/Canada system)
467.8250	457.6000	On-board-ship communications (US/Canada system)
467.8250 to 468.0000	455.0000 to 462.0000	Point-to-point links
468.5000 to 469.0000		Some Outside broadcast links, model control and reserved for future PMR expansion
469.0000 to 470.0000		Some Outside Broadcast link talkback and mobiles

Table 7.1/2 *continued*

From-to	Pairing	Allocation
470.0000–854.0000		UK Band IV Television broadcasting, Studio talkback systems, Radio Astronomy & Aeronautical radionavigation, USSR communication satellites
471.0000 to 585.0000		Television broadcasting Band IV
537.0000 to 544.0000	716.000 to 725.000	Studio talkback mobiles on unused broadcast channels
582.0000 to 590.0000		Aeronavigation ground radar (due to be phased-out by 1995)
590.0000 to 598.0000		Aeronavigation ground radar
598.0000 to 606.0000		Aeronavigation ground radar (due to be phased-out by 1995)
614.0000		Radio Astronomy (Cambridge & Jodrell Bank)
610.0000 to 890.0000		Television Broadcasting Band V
702.0000 to 726.0000		Soviet direct TV broadcast satellites
716.0000 to 725.0000	537.0000 to 544.0000	Studio talkback bases on unused broadcast channels

Table 7.1/2   *continued*

From-to	Pairing	Allocation
800.0000 to 1000.0000		Molniya Soviet communication satellites (data & NFM)
854.0000–862.0000		Fixed & land mobile
854.0000 to 862.0000		Outside broadcast links
862.0000–864.0000		Land mobile (emergency services)
864.0000–870.0000		Mobile (not aeronautical) & portable telephone system CT2
864.0000 to 868.000		System CT2 'Telepoint' portable telephones. Digital encoded speech using FSK. 40 Channels at 100KHz spacing
870.0000–889.0000		Fixed & Mobile (mostly military), Industrial, scientific & medical & Anti-theft devices. TACS (cellular telephone) in London area
872.0000 to 888.0000	917.0000 to 933.0000	TACS (London only)
886.0000 to 890.0000		Industrial, scientific & medical
888.0000 to 889.0000		Anti-theft devices (1/2Watt maximum)
890.0000–915.0000		Mobile (TACS Cellular telephone & Government)

Table 7.1/2   *continued*

From-to	Pairing	Allocation
890.0125 to 904.9875	935.0125 to 949.9875	Cellular telephone mobiles (Full Duplex NFM)
905.0000 to 915.0000	950.0000 to 960.0000	Reserved for Pan-European Cellular system
915.0000-934.0000		Fixed & Mobile (Government) & Space communications, E-TACS Cellular telephones (London area only) and new UK personal radio system
917.0000 to 933.000	872.0000 to 888.0000	TACS (London only)
922.75000 926.06000 928.40000		Mir/Salyut TV picture downlinks Mir/Salyut Voice & telecommand (NFM) Venera deep-space planetary probe
933.00000 to 935.00000		New UK personal radio system
934.0000-935.0000		UK UHF Citizens Band radio allocation. 20 Channels NFM Simplex (to be phased out)
935.0000-960.0000		Mobile (Cellular telephone)
935.0125 to 949.9875	890.0125 to 904.9875	Cellular telephone bases (Full Duplex NFM)
950.0000 to 960.0000	905.0000 to 915.0000	Reserved for Pan-European Cellular telephone system

Table 7.1/2   *continued*

From-to Pairing	Allocation
960.0000–1215.0000	Aeronavigation (Distance measuring equipment — DME) & TACANS (radar transponders — IFF)
1215.0000–1240.0000	Radiolocation and radionavigation by satellite
1240.0000–1296.0000	Radiolocation
1296.0000–1300.0000	Amateur Radio 23CM band (NFM, SSB, WBTY, etc)
1300.0000–1365.0000	Amateur Radio 23CM band & Radiolocation (government)
1365.0000–1427.0000	Radiolocation, Space research & satellite exploration
1400.0000 to 1427.0000	Earth exploration satellites, astronomy & space research
1427.0000–1429.0000	Fixed & Mobile (Government) & Earth-Space satellite links
1429.0000–1450.0000	Fixed & Mobile (Government)
1450.0000–1525.0000	Fixed & Mobile (telephony, telecontrol & telemetry)
1525.0000–1530.0000	Fixed & land mobile & satellites (space-earth)
1530.0000–1544.0000	Land mobile & maritime mobile satellite services (space-earth)
1544.0000–1545.0000	Mobile satellite services

Table 7.1/2   *continued*

From-to	Pairing	Allocation
1544.0000 to 1545.0000	1645.0000 to 1646.0000	Space-Earth distress service
1544.5000		NOAA9/10 Search & rescue beacon locator downlink
1545.0000–1559.9000		Aeronautical mobile satellite service
1559.0000–1626.5000		Aeronautical radionavigation & navigation satellites & radio astronomy
1626.5000–1645.0000		Maritime mobile satellite service
1645.0000–1646.5000		Mobile satellite service
1645.0000 to 1646.0000	1544.0000 to 1545.0000	Earth-Space distress
1646.5000–1660.0000		Aeronautical mobile, satellite services (uplinks) & astronomy
1660.0000–1668.0000		Fixed & mobile & astronomy
1668.0000–1670.0000		Fixed links (government) & astronomy
1670.0000–1700.0000		Fixed (PTO & government) & land mobile & meteorological satellites. Goes, NOAA and Meteosat transmissions — for details see satellite section
1700.0000–2000.0000		Fixed & land mobile (PTO & government), satellite operations & astronomy

There follows a glossary of abbreviations and definitions used in Table 7.1/2.

Aeronautical Distress Frequencies allocated solely for use by aircraft in distress.

Aeronautical mobile Allocations for communication between aircraft and ground stations. The main international band lies between 118-136MHz.

Aeronautical Radionavigation Radio beacons for aircraft navigation. They include VHF omni-range (VOR), doppler VOR (DVOR), distance measuring equipment (DME), instrument landing systems (ILS), tactical navigation (TACAN), outer, middle and inner fan markers (OM, MM, IM), etc.

Aeronautical search and rescue Frequencies allocated solely for aircraft involved in search and rescue (SAR) duties.

Amateur The amateur service is for use by licensed individuals for the purpose of self-training and experimentation.

Astronomy Frequencies allocated for research into radio emissions from sources such as other galaxies.

Broadcast Transmissions intended for reception by a large group or even the general public.

BT British Telecom.

Carphone A communication system fitted to a vehicle which communicates with a base station connected to the public telephone system.

Citizens Band A low powered communications service available to the public.

Cordless 'phone A telephone handset that does not require direct connection to the exchange line.

COSPAS/SARSAT Joint US, USSR, Canadian and French rescue service using weather satellite to fix the position of emergency rescue beacons.

CT2 see Telepoint

ELINT Electronic intelligence gathering (typically spy satellites).

Emergency service Allocations for police, fire and ambulance services.

EPIRB Emergency position indicating rescue beacon.

Fixed A base station linked to another base station or non-mobile facility such as a repeater. Often known as point-to-point services.

FSK Frequency shift keying.

IFF Identify — friend or foe.

ILR Independent local radio.

ISM Industrial, scientific and medical. These allocations are for equipment which use radio waves to function. These allocations are not for communication purposes.

Land Mobile Communications between a fixed base and mobile or portable equipment or between the mobile stations themselves.

Locator The transmission of signals for navigation, position fixing and tracking.

Maritime Mobile Services for ship-to-shore and ship-to-ship communications.

Message handling Similar to PMR but many stations operating through a central operator at a base station.

Meteorology The transmission of weather data from remote platforms such as sondes, buoys or satellites to ground stations.

Military British military allocations cover the army, Royal Air Force, Royal Navy, military police and United States Air Force (USAF).

Mobile Any mobile service. Air, marine or land.

Mobile satellite service Communication between a mobile station and satellite (usually the satellite is acting as a relay or repeater to a distant ground station).

MOD Ministry of Defence.

Model Control The use of radio signals to control the movement of model boats, aircraft and cars.

MOULD British military communication system making extensive use of repeaters.

NOAA National Oceanic and Atmospheric Administration (USA).

On-site paging A paging service operating in a restricted area such as a hospital, factory or hotel.

Pager A miniature radio receiver which emits a tone when it receives a signal with its individually assigned code.

Positioning aid A beacon used to emit a transmission for precise positioning or navigation. Often used for positioning such things as oil rigs.

PMR Private mobile radio. Allocations for non-government users for communication between base stations and mobile units.

Radio altimeter The use of radio signals to measure the height of an aircraft above ground.

Radio microphone A microphone used in broadcast studios, theatres and the film industry where the unit transmits the sound as a low powered radio signal which is picked-up by a remote receiver and then amplified.

Radiophone See Carphone.

SARBE Search and rescue beacon. A small radio beacon attached to a lifejacket or dinghy.

Satellite navigation Position fixing by reference to transmissions from a satellite.

Selcal Selective calling system where a receiver only activates when it receives a pre-determined code.

Slick marker A low powered floating beacon used to check the movement of oil slicks.

Standard frequency Transmission from a highly stable transmitter which is accurate enough to be used for calibration and reference. The signals often include coded signals of highly accurate time as well.

TACS Total access communications system (cellular telephones)

Telecontrol A signal containing command information to control remote equipment.

Telemetry A radio signal containing data in coded form.

Telepoint Cordless telephone service (similar to Cellular) available only when near an access point.

Television A radio signal containing visual images.

Weather satellite A space satellite that sends weather pictures back to an earth station.

Wide area paging A paging service not confined to a private site.

Aeronautical bands

Aeronautical and marine bands, unlike all other bands, are standard world wide. Aircraft transmissions are of two kinds: civilian and military.

Civilian aircraft transmissions use two bands: HF using SSB for long distance communication, and VHF for communications up to distances of several hundred miles. All communications (civilian and military) are amplitude modulated.

A list of civilian and military airports and corresponding transmission frequencies are given and are believed to be current. However, it should be noted that they are occasionally changed.

Update It has just been announced that the band is to be extended to 137MHz, but at the time of writing no details were available.

Table 7.3 British and Irish airports and ground stations

Airfield	LOC	ATIS	MATZ	APP	TWR	GND	VDF	RAD
Abbeyshrule (EI)								
Aberdeen	EGPD	121.850		120.400	122.600 / 118.100	A/G / 121.700	121.250 / 128.300	353.550 / 120.400
Aberporth (MOD)	EGUC		353.850 / 120.900	All AFIS				
Abingdon	EGUD	122.150		122.100	130.250 / 256.500			123.300 / 259.300 / 344.000
Aces High (N. Weald)			130.170	(Ops)				
Albuskjell (oil rig)					130.550	(helipad)		
Alconbury	EGWZ		134.050	122.100 / 257.800	361.550	339.250		
Alderney (CI)	EGJA			128.650	315.100 / 123.600	all tower		
Alwyn (oil rig)					130.200	(helipad)	122.350	(ops)
Andrewsfield Radio	EGSL				130.550	A/G	122.050	(ops)
Argyll (oil rig)					122.520	(helipad)		
Audley End					122.350			
Auk (oil rig)					122.520	(helipad)	122.050	(ops)
Bacton					123.450	(helipad)		
Badminton					130.420	A/G		
Banff					123.500	A/G		
Bantry (EI)					122.400	A/G		
Barkston Heath	EGYE		Cranwell	367.200	307.700			313.800
Barrow (Walney)	EGPR				123.200			
Beatrice (oil rig)					123.650	(helipad)		
Beccles	EGSM				134.600	A/G		
Bedford Thurleigh	EGVW		124.400	130.700 / 265.100 / 277.250	130.000 / 241.350		124.400 / 277.250 / 265.100	118.375 / 356.700 / 130.700

Airfield	LOC	ATIS	MATZ	APP	TWR	GND	VDF	RAD
Belfast (Aldergrove)	EGAA			120.000 / 353.300	118.300 / 353.300		120.900	120.000 / 353.300
Belfast (Harbour)	EGAC			130.850	130.750			122.450
Bembridge Radio	EGHJ				123.250	A/G		
Benbecula	EGPL	119.200	AFIS		119.200			
Benson	EGUB		120.900	122.100 / 299.100 / 362.300	122.100 / 398.700		120.900 / 259.300 / 299.100	123.300 / 354.800 / 314.400
Bentwaters (USAF)	EGVJ		119.000	119.000 / 292.700 / Departure	122.100 / 257.800 / 381.850	275.600		119.000 / 308.500
Beryl (oil rig)			356.000		123.000			
Biggin Hill	EGKB			129.400	134.800	(helipad)		132.700
Biggleswade					123.050	A/G	air shows	
Binbrook	EGXB		125.350	383.900	122.100 / 242.650 / 257.800		383.900 / 125.350	123.300 / 308.700 / 256.050
Birmingham	EGBB	112.900		120.500	118.300	121.800	120.500	118.050
Birr (EI)					122.900	A/G		
Bishops Court (N.I.)					354.150	A/G		
Blackbushe	EGLK	122.300	AFIS		118.400		118.400	119.950
Blackpool	EGNH			135.950	122.700			
Bodmin						A/G		
Boscombe Down	EGDM	370.850	126.700 / 264.500	126.700 / 264.500 / 228.200 / 282.800	130.000 / 242.200 / 126.700	313.200	126.700 / 264.500 / 340.000	130.750 / 290.550
Boulmer Rescue					285.850	all A/G		All Radar
Bourn	EGSN				129.800	A/G		
Bournemouth (Hurn)	EGHH	121.950	123.100	119.750	125.600	121.600	Fire	118.650
Bovingdon					243.800	A/G		

Station	Code						
Brae (oil rig)							
Brawdy	EGDA	124.400	122.100 124.400 362.300 292.000	123.650 122.100 243.300 257.800	(helipad) 245.900	122.320	(ops) 123.300 387.350 313.200 276.300 341.050
Brent (oil rig)				122.250 123.250	(helipad)	123.050	(ops)
Bridlington Radio					A/G		
Bristol Filton	EGTG	130.850 244.700	130.850 244.700	124.950 290.350		130.850 132.350	132.350 244.700
Bristol (Lulsgate)	EGGD		132.400 133.750 246.450 362.300	120.550		132.400 133.750	124.350 359.100
Brize Norton	EGVN	235.150 / 119.000		126.500 249.750 257.800	126.500 288.850	308.750 246.450 134.300	344.000 252.350 133.750
Brough	EGNB		118.250	130.550 310.350			
Bruntingthorpe				122.820	A/G		
Buchan (oil rig)				122.000	(helipad)		
Caernarfon Radio				122.250	A/G		
Cambridge	EGSC		123.600	122.200 341.800	121.600	Fire	130.750 341.800
Cardiff	EGFF		125.850 358.700	125.000 341.800			120.050 125.850
Carlisle	EGNC		123.600	123.600			
Carnmore (EI)				122.500	A/G		
Carrickfin (EI)				129.800	A/G		
Casement (EI)			122.000	123.500	A/G		
Castlebar (EI)				122.600	A/G		129.700
Castelbridge (EI)				123.000	A/G		
Chalgrove				125.400			
Chetwynd				363.400			
Chichester-Goodwood	EGHR		122.450	120.650			

Airfield	LOC	ATTIS	MATZ	APP	TWR	GND	VDF	RAD
Chivenor	EGDC		130.200, 122.100	309.900, 362.300	122.100, 286.950, 318.500	307.400	309.900, 381.400, 315.450	122.100, 381.400, 387.650, 123.300, 356.700, 385.400
Church Fenton	EGXG		126.500, 381.800, 362.300	381.800, 362.300	122.100, 359.800, 257.800			
Clacton					122.320, 122.450, 130.550	339.300	344.000	All Radar
Claymore (oil rig)						A/G (helipad)		
Cod (oil rig)						(helipad)		
Coltishall	EGYC		125.900, 379.200, 297.150	122.100, 361.650	122.100, 142.290, 288.850	284.575	125.900, 379.200, 361.650	123.300, 371.000, 275.450
Compton Abbas	EGHA				122.700	A/G		
Coningsby	EGXC		120.800, 370.900	122.100, 362.300, 345.150	121.100, 234.950, 120.800	122.100, 318.150		276.650, 344.000, 342.600, 358.100
Connaught (EI)	EIKN				130.700, 129.950	121.900		
Cormorant (oil rig)								
Cork (EI)	EICK			119.900	119.300, 121.700	(helipad), 121.800	123.050	(ops) 118.800
Cosford	EGWC			234.100, 362.300	292.100, 122.100			
Cottesmore	EGXJ		130.200, 266.050	354.400	122.100, 246.400, 257.800	122.100, 307.400	266.050, 130.200	123.300, 297.600, 317.700
Coventry	EGBE			370.450, 119.250	119.250, 123.200	124.800	122.000	122.000
Cranfield	EGTC			122.850, 372.100	341.800		122.850	122.850

Location	Code							
Cranwell	EGYD	119.000		122.100 297.900 362.300 119.000	380.100 257.800 362.100 119.000	276.000		364.500 344.000 267.200 316.100
Croughton (USAF)		305.600						
Culdrose	EGDR		134.050 122.100	292.700 130.400	343.600 123.300 289.100	A/G 310.200	251.100	246.300 256.500 All Radar
Cumbernauld					120.600	A/G		
Dan (oil rig)					123.450	A/G		
Dartmouth (R.N.)					287.050	(helipad)		
Denham Radio	EGLD				130.725	A/G		
Derby (Burnaston)	EGBD				118.350	A/G		
Dishforth	EGXD	See	Leeming		309.300	A/G		
Doncaster Radio					122.900	A/G		
Dounreay Thurso	EGPY			122.400	122.400	A/G		
Dublin (EI)	EIDW	127.000	Volmet	121.100	118.600	121.800		119.550 118.500
Dundalk				122.900				
Dundee	EGPN			122.900	122.900			
Dunkeswell					123.475	A/G		
Dunlin (oil rig)					129.950	(helipad)	123.050 122.550	(ops) 118.825
Dunsfold	EGTD			122.550 241.800	124.325 287.500			
Duxford	EGSR	123.500	AFIS			A/G		
Earls Colne Radio					122.425	A/G		
Easington					129.850	(helipad)		
East Midlands	EGNX			119.650 122.250 130.200 129.950	124.000	121.900	119.650	120.150
East Shetland Basin					Brent Ninian Viking			
Edinburgh	EGPH	132.075		121.200 130.400	118.700	121.750	118.700 121.200	121.200 128.975

Airfield	LOC	ATIS	MATZ	APP	TWR	GND	VDF	RAD
Ekofisk (oil rig)					130.550	(helipad)		
Ekofisk (Emden)					129.900	(helipad)		
Ekofisk (Teeside)					122.950	(helipad)		
Elstree Radio	EGTR				122.400	A/G		
Elvington	EGYK	See	Church	Fenton				
Eniskillen (St Angelo)	EGAB				123.200 129.875	A/G A/G		
Enstone					122.320	(helipad)		
Esmond (oil rig)						(helipad)		
Exeter	EGTE			128.150	119.800		128.150	119.050
Fairford (USAF)	EGVA		122.100	119.000 362.300 246.450	119.150 380.000 257.800	276.550		
Fairoaks Info	EGTF	123.425	AFIS					
Farnborough	EGUF	130.050	A/G	134.350 296.250 125.250	122.500 387.600 (transit)		125.250 275.550 130.050	296.250 359.700 353.850
Farnborough air show	UGUF			134.050 135.750	127.500	(helipad) 130.500	118.100	Depart
Farranfore (EI)					122.600	A/G		
Felden					129.750	(helipad)		
Fenland Info	EGCL	123.050	AFIS		123.050	A/G		
Fife (Glenrothes)	EGPJ				130.450	A/G		
Filton	EGXI	See	Bristol					
Finningley	EGXI		120.350 293.700	398.500 120.350	122.100 315.700	276.000		368.400 344.000 293.700
Fleetlands			135.700	394.200	340.750	A/G		
Flotta					122.150			
Forbes (oil rig)					122.320	(helipad)		
Forties (oil rig)					122.000	(helipad)		

Name	ICAO							
Foulsham				130.650	A/G			
Frigg (oil rig)				129.700	(helipad)			
Frig-Fergus (oil rig)				130.720	(helipad)			
Fulmar (oil rig)				122.520	(helipad)	122.050		(ops)
Fulmar Buoy (oil rig)				123.000	(helipad)			
Galway (EI)				122.500				
Gamston	EGNE	115.400		130.475	A/G			
Glasgow	EGPF		119.100	118.800	121.700	121.300	119.300	
Gloucester	EGBJ		125.650	125.650		125.650	122.900	
Gordon (oil rig)				122.320	(helipad)			
Gorm (oil rig)				123.450	(helipad)			
Great Yarmouth	EGSD	122.100		122.375	120.450	All A/G		
Greenham (USAF)	EGVI			266.800 358.350	276.550		257.500	
Grimsby				122.350	A/G			
Guernsey (CI)	EGJB	109.400	128.650	119.950	A/G	124.450	118.900	
Halfpenny Green	EGBO		123.000	A/G		118.900		
Hardwick				129.900	121.950			
Hatfield	EGTH		123.350 383.850	130.800 241.750	A/G		119.300 383.850	
Haverfordwest	EGFE			122.200	A/G			
Hawarden	EGNR	124.400	123.350	124.950 297.250	A/G	129.850	129.850	
Headfort (EI)				123.300	A/G			
Heather (oil rig)				122.800	(helipad)			
Henstridge	EGHS			130.275	A/G			
Hethel				122.350	A/G			
Hewett (oil rig)				122.870	(helipad)			
Hilcote				122.950	(helipad)			
Hitchin				122.350	A/G			
Honington	EGXH	129.050 361.600	355.350 362.300 361.600	122.100 233.850 257.800	318.150		369.350 344.000 241.550	

Airfield	LOC	ATIS	MATZ	APP	TWR	GND	VDF	RAD
Hucknall	EGNA				130.800	A/G		
Huddersfield					122.200	A/G		
Hull					129.900	A/G		
Humberside				123.150	118.550		123.150	
Hutton (oil rig)					130.800	(helipad)		
Indefatigable (oil rig)					123.620			
Inishmore (Aran)	EI				123.300	A/G		
Inverness (Dalcross)	EGPE			122.600	122.600			
Ipswich Radio	EGSE			118.325	118.325			
Islay (Port Ellen)	EGPI	123.150						
Isle of Man	EGNS		AFIS	120.850	118.900		118.200	125.300
					123.500			
					130.650			
Isle of Wight	EGHN					A/G		
Isle of Skye						A/G		
Jersey (CI)	EGJJ	112.200		120.300	119.450	121.900		125.200
				123.300	122.100			293.800
				363.100	335.550			363.950
				362.300				
Kemble	EGDK		122.100					
			363.100					
Kilkenny (EI)								
Kinloss	EGQK			119.350	122.900	130.400	All A/G	123.300
				319.000	122.100			352.500
				288.450	287.000			387.350
					257.800			
Kinsale East (oil rig)					123.450	(helipad)		
Kinsale West (oil rig)					123.450	(helipad)		
Kirkwall	EGPA			118.300	118.300			
Knock (EI)	see	Connaught						
Kyle (R.N.)				129.050	130.650	A/G		123.300
Lakenheath (USAF)	EGUL			379.800	122.100	248.450	355.700	149.650
					231.500			243.600
					257.800			
				315.600	309.000	344.000		all radar

Station	ICAO	Frequencies
Lands End (St Just)	EGHC	121.400
Lasham	EGKH	130.700 (all A/G)
Lashenden Radio		122.870 (A/G)
Leavesden	EGTI	122.150, 122.000, 121.400
Leconfield	ECXV	282.800, 369.650
Leeds/Bradford	EGNM	123.750, 120.300, 123.750, 359.200, 362.300, 387.800, 121.050, 132.400, 339.400
Leeming	EGXE	132.400, 387.800, 122.100, 382.100, 394.500
Lee-on-Solent	EGUS	AFIS 135.700, 340.500, All Tower
Leicester Radio	EGBG	122.250 (A/G)
Leith		122.250 (helipad)
Leman (oil rig)		123.620 (helipad)
Lerwick Tingwall		122.600 (A/G)
Leuchars	EGQL	126.500, 257.700, 126.500, 362.300, 122.100, 269.000, 120.800, 290.700, 122.100, 123.300, 252.300, 288.300, 318.100
Linton-on-Ouse	EGXU	129.150, 357.500, 362.300, 361.200, 122.100, 246.800, 257.800, 398.300, 335.700, 344.000, 288.100
Little Gransden		130.850
Liverpool	EGGP	119.850, 118.100 (A/G), 118.450
Llanbedr	EGOD	122.500, 365.900, 122.500, 294.600, 122.500, 365.900
London City	EGLC	119.425, 121.775, Thames, City, 132.700, 128.025
London Gatwick	EGKK	128.475, 125.875, 129.275, 124.225, 129.275, 121.800, 121.950, Clearance, 118.600, 119.600
London Heathrow	EGLL	121.850, 115.100, 113.750, 133.075, Departure, arrival, arrival, arrival, 119.200, 120.400, 119.500, 127.550, 118.700, 121.000, 121.900, 121.700 (radar), delivery
VFR & Helicopters		119.900, 119.200

Airfield	LOC	ATIS	MATZ	APP	TWR	GND	VDF	RAD
London Stansted	EGSS	127.175		125.550	118.150	121.600	126.950	123.800
London Heliport	EGLW				122.900			
Londonderry	EGAE			122.850	122.850			
Lossiemouth	EGQS		119.350	319.000	118.900	314.400	318.500	123.300
			394.100	362.300	122.100		319.000	315.100
				398.100	291.000		119.350	286.550
				119.350				318.500
Luton	EGGW	133.975		129.550	120.200	121.750	127.300	127.300
				129.750	398.000		120.200	128.750
Lydd	EGMD			120.700	120.700			131.300
Lyneham	EGDL	367.600		118.425	118.425	122.100	123.400	360.650
				315.750	293.100	318.950		383.400
				362.300	122.100	118.425		276.350
				123.400				344.000
Machrihanish	EGQJ		125.900	122.100	122.100			123.300
				287.050	285.600			354.200
				362.300	257.800			385.400
				289.600				344.000
Magnus (oil rig)				All AFIS		(helipad)		
Malvern		120.000	317.900	119.400	122.370			121.350
Manchester Intl	EGCC	128.175			118.700	121.700		
Manchester Barton	EGCB				122.700	A/G		
Manston Civilian	EGMH	common	channels	126.350	124.900		129.450	126.350
Manston Military	EGUM			122.100	362.100		126.350	123.300
				352.500	257.800		352.500	290.300
				362.300	122.100		290.300	385.400
								387.000
Marham	EGYM		124.150	265.800	122.100		124.150	317.950
				362.300	275.350		122.100	385.400
				124.150	257.800		265.800	340.750

Location	ICAO						
Maureen (oil rig)				123.550	(helipad)		
Merryfield			122.100	287.100			
Middle Wallop	EGVP	Boscombe	126.700	122.100	All tower	362.300	280.400
			314.900	267.100			365.300
Mildenhall (USAF)	EGUN		129.050	257.800	297.400		
			353.350	122.550			
				250.000			
Molesworth				328.400	(ops)		
Mona	See	Valley					
Montrose (oil rig)				129.700	(helipad)		
Morecambe (oil rig)				122.370	(helipad)		
Murchison (oil rig)				122.050	(helipad)		
Nam (oil rig)				122.950	(helipad)		
Naphill				267.450	(helipad)		
Netheravon	EGDN		254.000	128.300			
				233.400			
Nether Thorpe	EGNF	114.250		123.500	A/G		
Newcastle	EGNT		126.350	119.700		118.500	126.350
			397.100			119.700	118.500
Newton	EGXN	122.100	362.300	300.400			
			292.900	257.800			
Newtownards Radio	EGAD			123.500	A/G		
Ninian (oil rig)				130.200	(helipad)	122.050	(ops)
Noordwinning (oil rig)				122.950	(helipad)		
Nordsee (oil rig)				129.750	(helipad)		
Northampton Sywell	EGBK	268.900		122.700	A/G		
Northolt			134.150	275.650		134.150	130.350
			377.500	257.800		377.500	355.400
			362.300	134.150			244.550
North Weald				123.520	A/G	130.500	air shows
Norwich	EGSH		119.350	118.900		119.350	124.250
Nottingham Radio				122.800	A/G		
Nottingham Springfield				123.050	(helipad)		

Airfield	LOC	ATIS	MATZ	APP	TWR	GND	VDF	RAD
Oban					130.400			
Odiham	EGVO	269.700	125.250	122.100	378.550			123.300
			318.100	341.000	257.800			364.050
				362.300	122.100			385.400
				125.250				275.550
Old Sarum						A/G		
Oranmore (El)						A/G		
Oxford (Kiddington)	EGTK	121.950		130.300	123.575		130.300	
		119.800			123.600			
					119.800	121.750		
Oxford (college)					132.650	A/G		
Oxford Weston					133.650	255.100	all A/G	
Pailton Test	EGBP				126.050	A/G		
Panshanger Info	EGLG				120.250	A/G		
Paull					123.000	A/G		
Penzance Heliport	EGHK				118.100	A/G		
Perth (Scone)	EGPT			122.300	119.800		122.300	
Peterborough (Con)	EGSF				123.000	A/G		
Peterborough (Sib)	EGSP				122.300	A/G		
Peterhead					122.370	(helipad)		
Petroland (oil rig)					122.950	(helipad)		
Placid (oil rig)					122.950	(helipad)		
Plockton					122.370	A/G		
Plymouth	EGHD				122.600			
Plymouth (R.N.)		244.600	282.800	133.550	382.900	A/G		
				All SAR				
Pocklington					130.100	A/G		
Popham Radio					129.800	A/G		
Portland	EGDP	282.800	124.150	124.150	122.100			387.500
			A/G	122.100	123.300			362.300
				317.800	291.000			317.800
				362.300	362.300			124.150

Location	Code							
Porton								
Predannack	EGDR							
Prestwick	EGPK	See		120.550	313.700	353.900	all helipad	119.450
					364.700			
Prestwick (R.N.)			Culdrose		118.150			
Redhill Info	EGKR	123.225			291.000	(ops)		
Retford-Gamston	EGNE		AFIS		130.475	A/G		
Rochester Info					122.250	A/G		
Rona					130.650	A/G		
Rough (oil rig)					129.870	(helipad)		
Rufforth					130.400	A/G		
St. Athan	EGDX			122.100	122.100			123.300
				280.300	352.900			352.400
				362.300	257.800			385.400
				344.000				277.600
St. Kilda								
St. Mawgan	EGDG		126.500	122.100	128.100		126.500	394.500
				125.550	123.400		125.550	123.300
				352.850	122.100		352.850	385.400
				362.300	286.200		387.850	387.750
								344.000
Salisbury Plain	EGNG				130.150	253.500	All A/G	
Samlesbury	EGCF			124.450	130.350			
Sandtoft Radio					130.425	A/G		
Scampton	EGXP		127.350	314.800	362.500	307.400	243.300	265.900
Scatsta	EGPM			123.600	123.600	121.600	Fire	122.400
Scilly Isles				123.150	123.150			
Sculthorpe	EGHE		264.250	246.700	378.050	277.600		250.300
Sean (oil rig)					123.620	(helipad)		
Seething Radio					122.600	A/G		
Shannon (EI)	EINN	130.950		121.400	118.700	121.800	Oceanic	121.400
				120.200				121.700

Airfield	LOC	ATIS	MATZ	APP	TWR	GND	VDF	RAD
Shawbury	EGOS		124.150 251.500	124.150 364.100 362.300	122.100 359.200 257.800	382.200		256.200 344.000 123.300 341.600 385.400
Shendish					129.750	A/G		
Sherburn Radio	EGCJ				122.600	A/G		
Shipdam					123.050	A/G		
Shobdon Radio	EGBS				123.500	A/G		
Shoreham	EGKA			123.150	125.400		123.150	
Silverstone					121.075			
Skegness					130.450	A/G		
SKJO (oil rig)					123.450	(helipad)		
Sleap					122.450	A/G		
Sligo (EI)					122.100	A/G		
Southampton	EGHI	121.300	Zone	128.850	118.200			131.000
Southend	EGMC			128.950	119.700		128.950	125.050
South Marston	EGLF	130.425	AFIS		130.425	A/G		
Stanford Ops (army)					314.550	A/G		
Stapleford	EGSG				122.800	A/G		
Stornoway	EGPO			123.500	123.500			
Strathallen Radio					123.500	A/G		
Strubby	EGCG				122.370	(helipad)	130.100	A/G
Sturgate Radio	EGPB				130.300	A/G		
Sumburgh	EGPB	125.850		123.150	118.250			119.250
Swansea	EGFH			119.700	119.700		119.700	120.750
Swanton Morley					123.500			
Swinderby				307.100	313.300	122.100	Tower	
Tartan (oil rig)					122.450	(helipad)		
Tatenhill					122.200	A/G		

Location	ICAO	Frequencies / notes
Tees-Side	EGNY	118.850, 119.800, 128.850, 300.000
Ternhill		336.200
Thirsk		130.400
Thistle (oil rig)		A/G
Thruxton Radio		122.050 (helipad)
Tibenham		A/G, 130.450
Tiree	EGHO	130.100, 130.400
Topcliffe	EGPU	AFIS, 122.700
Topcliffe	EGXZ	Leeming, all A/G, 125.000, 122.100, 293.100, 257.800, 382.600, 362.300, 123.300, 290.800, 385.400
Tor (oil rig)		(helipad)
Tresco		(helipad)
Trim (EI)		A/G, 130.550, 122.950, 123.300
Trinity House		lighthouse, 129.700
Unst (Shetland)	EGPW	helipads, 130.500
Upavon		263.950, 357.000
Upper Heyford	EGUA	122.100, 313.650, 257.800, 128.550, 316.850, 362.300, 309.700, 259.850, 234.600, 294.550, 369.100, 395.050
Valley	EGOV	134.350, 122.100, 307.400, 257.800, 378.900, 362.300, 387.500, 285.450, 385.400, 319.000
Viking (oil rig)		(helipad)
Waddington	EGXW	127.350, 123.570, 122.100, 383.600, 257.800, 247.900, 362.300, 258.550, 344.000, 385.400, 258.850
Warton	EGNO	124.450, 130.800, 286.750, 254.350

Airfield	LOC	ATIS	MATZ	APP	TWR	GND	VDF	RAD
Waterford (EI)					129.850	A/G		
Wattisham	EGUW		123.400	123.400 299.200 362.300	122.100 353.500		123.400 299.200	355.050 286.200 300.250 344.000
Wellesbourne	EGBW				130.450	A/G	130.450	
West Freugh (MOD)	EGOY		130.050	130.050 387.550	122.550 241.350			387.550 353.850
West Malling					130.420	A/G	130.500	air shows
Weston (EI)					122.400	A/G		
Weston	EGFI			129.250	122.500			
West Sole (oil rig)					129.870	(helipad) 308.100		
Wethersfield	EGVT		122.100	362.300 387.400 344.150	122.100 293.600 257.800	369.500	380.900	123.300 230.700 296.600
Weybridge	EGLM				130.370	A/G		All radar
Whitechurch	EGPC				130.400	A/G		
White Waltham	EGNW				122.600	A/G		
Wick		119.700	AFIS		119.700			
Wickenby Radio					122.450	A/G		
Winfield					123.500	A/G		
Wittering	EGXT		130.200	130.200 142.290 382.750 362.300	122.100 142.290 251.030 257.800	318.150		123.300 363.150 316.000
Woodbridge	EGVG			255.800	119.150 122.100 257.800 291.350	307.400		

Name	ICAO							
Woodford	EGCD			130.050, 122.500, 243.400, 336.600	126.925, 130.500, 336.600, 243.400			130.750, 130.050, 336.600, 243.400
Woodvale	EGOW			120.650, 133.650	233.100, 315.100	344.800	All Tower	
Wroughton								
Wycombe Air Park								
Wyton	EGTB	126.550				121.600		
	EGUY		AFIS 134.050	134.050, 338.100, 362.300	122.100, 251.100, 257.800	286.050		277.750, 385.400, 344.000, 267.750
Yeovil	EGHG			130.800, 287.800	125.400, 341.800			130.800, 226.000
Yeovilton	EGDY	364.800	127.350, 276.700	127.350, 362.300, 276.700	122.100, 381.000, 234.300	265.700	127.350, 276.700	123.300, 340.400, 234.300
						259.600	362.300	All radar

If an aerial is used solely for airband reception then it should be vertically polarised. It is worth noting, by the way, that a simple ground plane aerial of the type described in Chapter 5 is more than adequate for aircraft band-only operation.

What you might hear

Remember that aircraft transmissions are usually short and there may be long periods when nothing is heard on a frequency. This applies, in particular, to smaller airfields where traffic movement may be quite low.

In addition to approach, control tower and radar landing instructions you may also hear a variety of other messages being passed on other frequencies in the bands. Many airlines have 'company frequencies' on which aircraft crews and ground operation staff communicate. You may also hear transmissions relating to zone, area or sector controllers. These are the people who control the movements of aircraft as they fly between airports. Different sectors have different transmission frequencies and so, to follow a particular aircraft as it moves from one sector to another, you will need to change your reception frequencies, to suit.

At London Heathrow and similar large airports, the sheer volume of traffic means that instructions passed to the aircraft must be done by several controllers and so you may come across frequencies which are dealing solely with such things as instructions on taxiing on the ground.

Continuous transmissions

Some frequencies are allocated solely for transmissions from the ground. The aircraft never transmit on these frequencies but the crews may listen to the broadcasts for information. The most common of these are 'VOLMETS', transmitted round the clock and detailing current weather conditions for most major airports.

Automatic terminal information service (ATIS) transmissions, on the other hand, are sent out by individual airports and only include details of that airport, including current weather, runway and approach patterns in use, and any other essential information. They, in fact, contain all the information a pilot needs except actual landing permission. Pilots will listen to these transmissions and when contacting the controller will often be heard to say such things as 'information Bravo received'. The word 'Bravo' standing for the code letter which identifies the start of an ATIS transmission. ATIS transmissions are made in the navigation aid band (108-118MHz).

Range

As we mentioned earlier in the book, range is difficult to define as it is affected by so many factors. Using a reasonable outside aerial it may be possible to hear ground stations up to 20 miles or so away. However, if hills or large buildings are between the scanner and the airport then this range will be considerably reduced. For instance, in my own case I cannot pick up my local airport which is only four miles away and yet can pick up another airport which is some 25 miles away in a different direction.

Air-to-ground range though is a different matter altogether. Aircraft flying at tens of thousands of feet may be heard several hundred miles away even though the scanner is only operating on a small telescopic aerial. This is because the line-of-site range is greatly extended by the height of the aircraft which is transmitting from a point where there are no obstructions to block or weaken the signal.

You will hear many unfamiliar expressions and considerable use of abbreviations in the airband. If you are not familiar with these, you can look them up in the airband section in Chapter 8.

Notes on civilian airport frequencies
Occasionally frequencies may be interchanged and, for instance, approach control will be handled by the tower. However, all the air-fields shown do have their main frequencies listed. A/G (Air/Ground stations) are for the most part communication stations available at smaller airfields. Pilots can call these facilities to obtain current weather information and the operator may well also warn of any other aircraft that are in the circuit. However, unlike an air traffic controller, the operator is not licensed to give the pilot landing instructions and it is up to the pilot to keep a look-out and make sure that he is not going to endanger any other aircraft during landing or take-off.

Military airport transmissions
Military airport transmissions use the same frequencies as civilian airports, but also have frequency allocations between 240 and 350MHz.

Table 7.4 Special military allocations

Facility	Frequency (MHz)		
Aces High Ops (N. Weald)	130.175		
Boulmer Rescue	123.100	282.800	285.850
Dalcross Tower (range)	122.600		
Deptford Down control	247.100		
Distress (army)	40.0500		
Distress (including beacons)	243.000		
Distress (UK only)	244.600		
Donna Nook Range	123.050		
Falcons display team	255.100		
Garvie Range	353.250		
Leconfield Rescue centre	282.800	369.650	
Lee-on-Solent rescue	132.650		
Manorbier Range	226.500	278.800	
NATO emergency	243.000	282.800	40.050

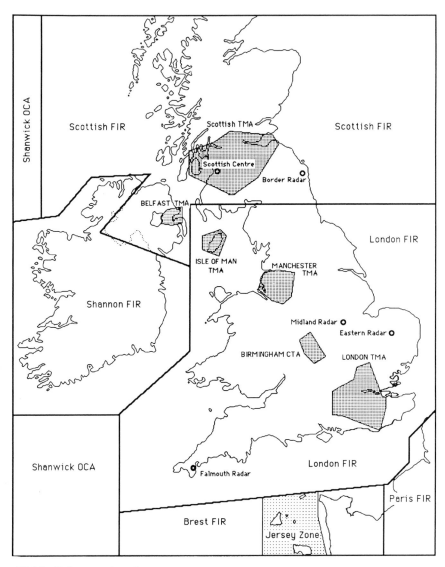

Table 7.4   *continued*

Facility	Frequency (MHz)	
NATO low level manouvres	273.900	
NATO SAR training	253.800	
NATO standard approach	362.300	
NATO standard radar	385.400	344.000
NATO standard Tower	257.800	
Neatishead (range warning)	123.100	
Plymouth (scene of Search)	244.600	282.800
Red Arrows (air-to-air)	243.450	
Rosehearty Range	354.850	

Table 7.4   *continued*

Facility	Frequency (MHz)		
SAR co-ordination air/sea	123.100		
Sharks display team (air to air)		388.000	
Spadeadam Range	122.100	241.250	
Standard Mil Field frequency	122.100	123.300	
Train Range	118.900	248.700	354.250
Wembury Range control	122.100		

Table 7.4b UK lower airspace radar advisory service (LARS)

Bedford	124.400	Farnborough	125.200	Newcastle	126.350
Binbrook	125.350	Finningley	120.350	Portland	124.150
Boscombe Down	126.700	Gatwick	119.600	St. Mawgan	126.500
Brawdy	124.400	Leuchars	126.500	Shawbury	124.150
Brize Norton	134.300	Linton-on-Ouse	129.150	Valley	134.350
Chivenor	130.200	Lossiemouth	119.350	Waddington	127.350
Coltishall	125.900	Luton	129.550	Warton	124.450
Cottesmore	130.200	Machrihanish	125.900	Wattisham	123.400
Culdrose	134.050	Manston	126.350	Wyton	134.050
Dunsfold	122.250	Marham	124.150	Yeovilton	127.350

Available to all aircraft in unregulated airspace up to and including Flight Level 95. The service provides advice for pilots on any other aircraft in the area covered by the radar of the ground station.

Table 7.4c UK military middle airspace radar advisory service

Border Radar	134.300	Highland Radar	134.300	Midland Radar	132.350
Brize Norton	128.425	London Military	124.750	Scottish Military	134.300
Eastern Radar	134.300	London Military	134.700		

Similar to LARS but offering a service to aircraft operating outside regulated airspace between Flight Levels 100 and 240.

Table 7.4d UK military danger area activity information service (DAAIS)

Aberdeen	120.400	Donna Nook	123.050	Neatishead	123.100
Aberporth	122.150	Edinburgh	121.200	Newcastle	126.350
Bentwaters	119.000	Farnborough	125.250	Portland	124.150
Border Info	134.850	Goodwood	122.450	St. Mawgan	126.500
Border Info	132.900	Leeming	132.400	Salisbury Plain	130.150
Boscombe Down	126.700	Leuchars	126.500	Scottish Mil	124.900
Brawdy	124.400	Liverpool	119.850	Scottish Mil	133.200
Bristol	127.750	Llanbedr Radar	122.500	Train Range	118.900
Brize Radar	134.300	London Info	124.600	Waddington	127.350
Chivenor	130.200	London Info	134.700	Wembury Range	122.100
Culdrose	134.050	Lydd	120.700	West Freugh	130.050
Dalcross Tower	122.600	Lyneham	123.400	Yeovilton	127.350

These stations provide information on the military training areas closest to them. Training ranges are used for a variety of purposes including gunnery on the ground, at sea and in the air. The airspace above the ranges is often closed to non-military aircraft and civilian pilots will call the above stations to determine whether or not they can fly through the areas.

MATZ stands for 'military aerodrome traffic zone' and civilian aircraft are not allowed in these areas without permission. Calls to obtain permission will be made on the MATZ frequency shown.

As with the civilian listing, many of the frequencies are interchangeable and it is not unusual for, say, the MATZ frequency to also be used for approach control or radar services.

Miscellaneous airband services

In addition to general airport approach, take off and landing services, there are a wide variety of other services. Aircraft need to be passed from one region to another and their use of designated airways needs to be controlled. When an aircraft is approaching London, for instance, it will have to change frequencies several times as it is handed from one sector to another. Crossing the borders of different countries also means a change of frequency to a new ground controller. Following an aircraft is easy as it is standard procedure in airband communication for the ground controller to tell the pilot which frequency to change to and for the pilot to repeat the frequency he has been given.

Table 7.5 lists a selection of controller frequencies in the UK and Ireland.

Table 7.5 UK and Irish ground control frequencies

Ground Control	(MHz)	Coverage
Anglia Radar	25.275	East Anglia/Southern N. Sea
	128.925	
	306.400	
	285.500	
Brize Norton ACC	134.300	Brize and Fairford areas
	119.000	
	308.750	
Dublin	128.000	ACC
	124.650	ACC
	128.000	Radar
	119.550	Radar
Eastern Radar	128.425	ACC
(Watton)	135.200	ACC
	288.500	Mil
Falmouth Radar	134.050	
	292.700	
	367.700	
Highland Radar	134.100	North Sea offshore advisory & Upper airspace
(Buchan)	126.100	North Sea offshore advisory
	134.300	Mil and advisory service
Jersey Zone	125.200	ATC in special rules area up to FL20
	120.450	ATC in special rules area up to FL20
	118.550	Radar
	120.300	Radar
Kent Radar	129.450	Cross Channel special rules airspace
London ACC	126.825	Below FL130 in Daventry CTA and London TMA
	123.900	Inbound via WILLO
	128.400	Inbound via Biggin & Eastwood
	126.450	Inbound via Biggin & Eastwood
	125.800	Inbound via Lambourne
	125.950	Inbound via Lambourne
	128.900	Inbound via Bovingdon
	126.300	Inbound via Bovingdon
	132.050	Inbound via Ockham
	125.800	Outbound via Brookmans Park
	128.400	Outbound via Detling & Hornchurch
	128.900	Outbound via Bovingdon
	132.050	Outbound via Woodley
	119.200	Helicopters & special VFR

Table 7.5   *continued*

Ground Control	(MHz)	Coverage
London Information (FIR)	124.750	West of Amber 47 & South of Blue 1
	124.600	East of Amber 47 & South of Blue 1
	134.700	North of Blue 1
	132.600	West of Upper Amber 47 & South of Upper Blue 1
	131.050	East of Upper Blue 4 & North of Upper Red 123
	134.250	South & North of Upper Blue 1
	285.950	UHF East of London
	267.000	UHF South East of London
	289.150	UHF South West of London
London Military	250.600	North of London
	342.800	South of London
Manchester Sub-centre	124.200	ATC
	125.100	ATC
	133.050	ATC
	126.650	ATC
	133.400	ATC
Midland Radar	132.250	
	134.300	
	307.500	
Penine Radar	132.900	ATC south of White 911D
Saxa Vord		See Shetland Radar
Scottish UACC	135.850	
	124.050	
	124.500	
Scottish Information	133.200	
	124.900	
	131.300	Northern North Sea sector
	128.500	North of White 911D
	124.500	Southern North Sea sector
Shannon ACC	131.150	Cork sector
	135.600	Shannon sector
	132.150	Eagle sector
	124.700	
	127.500	
	127.900	

Table 7.5 *continued*

Ground Control	(MHz)	Coverage
Shanwick Oceanic	127.900	East of 20' West
	123.950	West of 30' West
	127.650	East of 30' West
	135.525	
Oceanic tracks	133.800	Broadcasts
Shetland Radar	118.150	
	134.150	
	129.950	Below FL85
	285.650	Mil
Southampton Zone	121.300	ACC

Emergency frequencies

Table 7.6 lists the allocated UK emergency frequencies and services.

In addition to being allocated for emergency communications use, frequencies 121.5MHz and 243.0MHz are also used for search and rescue beacons of three forms. The first is a small transmitter emitting a radio bleep. It is triggered automatically when a crash occurs, or may be switched on manually. The second type contains a voice transmitter. The third type also includes a receiver, so turning it onto a full, two-way communications transceiver. These beacons are either hand-held or, in the case of SARBE versions, fitted to lifejackets.

Frequencies 156.0MHz and 156.8MHz (both marine frequencies) are used by search and rescue aircraft to communicate with lifeboats, etc.

Table 7.6 Emergency frequencies and services

Service	Frequencies (MHz)
Civilian	121.500
Boulmer Rescue	123.100-285.850-233.700-282.800
Leconfield Rescue	122.100-369.650-282.800
Lifeboat/coastguard	156.000 (FM)
Marine distress	156.800 (FM)
Military	243.000-40.0500
NATO (scene of search)	282.800
Search and rescue (air)	123.100

Navigational aids

Between the frequencies 108MHz and 117.95MHz you will hear a variety of navigational aids. These are VHF omni-range beacons (VOR) and instrument landing systems (ILS). Some of these services are paired with navigational aids on other bands to give additional services such as distance measuring (DME). Combined VOR/DME services are called VORTACS — the TAC part being a shortening of TACAN which in turn stands for 'tactical navigation'.

Although it *is* possible to hear these beacons, lists have not been included as they are not of interest to scanner users. The signals consist of nothing more than a short sequence of letters transmitted over and over again in morse code.

Table 7.7 VOLMETS providing weather information

Service	Frequency (MHz)
London VOLMET main	135.375
London VOLMET north	126.600
London VOLMET south	128.600
Dublin VOLMET	127.000

Table 7.7b Miscellaneous airband allocations

Service	Frequency (MHz)
Air-to-Air	123.450
Air-to-Air (North Atlantic only)	131.800
Balloons (hot air)	129.900
Distress	121.500
Fisheries protection surveillance	122.100 (North Sea)
	131.800 (S.W approaches and Channel)
Fire vehicles	121.600
Gliders	130.100, 130.125, 130.400
Ground control	121.700, 121.800, 121.900
Hang gliders	129.900
Lighthouse helipads	129.700
Search and Rescue (SAR)	123.100

VOLMETS

These are transmit-only stations providing constantly updated weather information for a variety of major airports. They are listed in Table 7.7.

Marine band

This, like the VHF airband, is one of the few international bands; it is common to *all* ITU regions.

It is channelised in that radio equipment made for marine VHF use does not usually have facilities to tune to a given frequency, instead it has a channel selector which goes from channel 1 to channel 88. A list of marine band channels and their transmission frequencies is given in Table 7.8.

Channels are designated for specific uses in that some are for ship-to-shore use, others for ship-to-ship, and so forth. The method of operating on marine band is very different from airband. On marine bands there is a common calling frequency which is also the main distress frequency: channel 16, at 156.8MHz. When a ship wishes to call a shore station, even though the operator may know the channel that is used by that shore station, he will still make first contact on channel 16. Once contact is made the ship and shore station will then move to a 'working channel' — in most instances this will be the station's 'prime' channel for general transmissions, or 'link' channel for link calls (ie, ship-to-shore telephone calls).

Channels 0 and 67 are used by lifeboats and coast guard vessels. Some search and rescue aircraft also have the facility to work these channels.

Table 7.8 shows that many channels have two frequencies. This is to enable duplex operation. Because these *are* duplex transmissions, it is impossible for a scanner to simultaneously monitor both frequencies. Two scanners would have to be used, each tuned to one of the two frequencies, if the whole transmission was to be received.

Range

The useful range for marine VHF communications tends to be somewhat better than for the same type of frequencies and power levels used across land. Quite simply, there are few obstructions at sea and maximum ranges of 50-100 miles are not unusual. However, while signals from a ship may be quite strong at a coastal station, the signals may deteriorate even a mile or two inland.

Table 7.8 International marine band channels and frequencies

Channel	Ship TX	Coast TX	Service
0	156.000		Coastguard/Lifeboat
1	156.050	160.650	Port Operation/Public Correspondence
2	156.100	160.700	Port Operation/Public Correspondence
3	156.150	160.750	Port Operation/Public Correspondence
4	156.200	160.800	Port Operation/Public Correspondence
5	156.250	160.850	Port Operation/Public Correspondence
6	156.300		Intership
7	156.350	160.950	Port Operation/Public Correspondence

Table 7.8 *continued*

Channel	Ship TX	Coast TX	Service
8	156.400		Intership
9	156.450		Intership
10	156.500		Intership
11	156.550		Port Operations
12	156.600		Port Operations
13	156.650		Port Operations
14	156.700		Port Operations
15	156.750		Port Operations
16	156.800		Distress and Calling
17	156.850		Port Operations
18	156.900	161.500	Port Operations
19	156.950	161.550	Port Operations
20	157.000	161.600	Port Operations
21	157.050	161.650	Port Operations
22	157.100	161.700	Port Operations
23	157.150	161.750	Public Correspondence
24	157.200	161.800	Public Correspondence
25	157.250	161.850	Public Correspondence
26	157.300	161.900	Public Correspondence
27	157.350	161.950	Public Correspondence
28	157.400	161.200	Public Correspondence
60	156.025	160.625	Public Correspondence
61	156.075	160.675	Public Correspondence
62	156.125	160.725	Public Correspondence
63	156.175	160.775	Public Correspondence
64	156.225	160.825	Public Correspondence
65	156.275	160.875	Public Correspondence
66	156.325	160.925	Public Correspondence
67	156.375		Intership/Small yacht safety/Coastguard
68	156.425		Intership
69	156.475		Intership
70	156.525		Digital Selective Calling/Distress
71	156.575		Port Operations
72	156.625		Intership
73	156.675		Intership
74	156.725		Port Operations, lock keepers, swing bridges
77	156.875		Intership
78	156.925	161.525	Port Operations
79	156.975	161.575	Port Operations
80	157.025	161.625	Port Operations
81	157.075	161.675	Port Operations
82	157.125	161.725	Port Operations
83	157.175	161.775	Port Operations
84	157.225	161.825	Port Operations
85	157.275	161.875	Port Operations
86	157.325	161.925	Public Correspondence
87	157.375	161.975	Public Correspondence
88	157.425	162.025	Public Correspondence
M	157.850		Marinas
M2	161.675		Marinas and yacht clubs

Table 7.9 General marine services and channel allocations

Service	Channels
Ship-to-ship	6, 8, 9, 10, 13, 15, 17, 67, 68, 70, 72, 75, 76, 77, 78
Port operations (simplex)	9, 10, 11, 12, 13, 14, 15, 17, 67, 69, 71, 73, 74
Port operations (duplex)	1, 2, 3, 4, 5, 7, 18, 19, 20, 21, 22, 60, 61, 62, 63, 64, 65, 66, 78, 79, 80, 81, 82, 84
Public correspondence (link calls)	1, 2, 3, 4, 5, 7, 23, 24, 25, 26, 27, 28, 60, 61, 62, 63, 64, 65, 66, 82, 83, 84, 85, 86, 87, 88

Shore stations

Table 7.10 lists UK shore stations, together with their Broadcast and working channels. All stations transmit local area navigation warnings (beacons out of action, hazardous floating objects, etc). Most, but not all, transmit local area weather forecasts and storm warnings.

Table 7.10 UK shore stations, prime and link channels

Station	Broadcast channel	Working channel
Anglesea	26	28/61
Bacton	07	63/64/03
Buchan	25	87
Cardigan Bay	03	28
Celtic	24	
Clyde	26	
Collafirth	24	
Cromarty	28	84
Cullercoats	26	
Forth	24	
Grimsby	27	04
Hastings	07	63
Hebrides	26	
Humber	26	24/85
Ilfracombe	05	07
Islay	25	
Jersey (CI)	25/82	67
Lands End	27	64/85/88
Lewis	05	
Malin Head	23	67/85/28/24/23
Morcambe Bay	04	82
Niton	28	81/85/04
N. Foreland	26	05/66/65
Orfordness	62	82
Orkney	26	
Pendennis	62	
Portpatrick	27	
Scillies	61	66
Severn	25	
Shetland	27	
Skye	24	
Start Point	26	60/65
St Helier Port (CI)	14	
St Peter Port (CI)	78	78/62
Stonehaven	26	
Thames	02	83
Weymouth Bay	05	05
Whitby	25	28

Principal simplex allocations

Table 7.11 lists principal simplex services' allocated channels.

Table 7.11 Principal simplex services' channel allocations

Service	Channel
Calling and distress	16
Port operations (prime)	12
Port operations (alternative)	14
Small yacht safety	67
Marinas	M/M2
Inter-ship (prime)	06
Inter-ship (alternative)	08

Amateur bands

Most general-purpose scanners will cover at least one of the VHF/UHF amateur bands. Although many scanner users may look to such things as air and marine bands as being the more exciting listening, amateur bands do have an attraction in that the operators are not subject to the same power restrictions, and so even at VHF and UHF amateur radio becomes international in its coverage. During the summer months, in particular, effects such as sporadic-E and tropospherical ducting can mean that signals can be picked up over several hundreds of miles.

British amateurs are restricted at VHF and UHF to 4 bands; 6 metre, 4 metre, 2 metre and 70 centimetre. There are other bands but these are beyond the coverage of most scanners.

6 metre band

The 6 metre band became available to British amateurs on the 1st of February, 1985, on an allocation between 50.0 and 52.00MHz.

Table 7.12 RSGB recommended frequency allocations

Frequency (MHz)	Allocation
50.000—50.100	CW and beacons only
50.100—50.500	Narrowband modes (SSB calling on 50.200)
50.500—51.000	All modes
51.000—51.100	Pacific DX window
51.100—52.000	All modes

This particular band is also available to amateurs in countries in Regions 2 and 3 (including the USA). There, the band lies between 50—54MHz and many amateurs claim that because it is lower in frequency than 2 metre and 4 metre bands it should be possible at times at achieve very good distances. The Gibraltar beacon for example ZB2VHF, on 50.035MHz, is regularly heard in Britain. Transatlantic communications have also been achieved, at these frequencies, in the past.

4 metre band

This band is one of the least used by amateurs, although the Amateur Radio Emergency Network, RAYNET, does favour it in some areas. Possibly one reason why it is not popular is that Britain is one of the few countries in the world with an allocation at these frequencies and so little if any international working is possible. The band extends from 70.025 to 70.5MHz and the only allocations are as given in Table 7.13.

Table 7.13 UK frequency allocations on the 4 metre band

Frequency (MHz)	Allocation
70.025—70.075	Beacons only
70.075—70.150	CW only
70.105—70.260	SSB and CW only
70.200	SSB calling frequency
70.260—70.400	All modes
70.260	Mobile calling frequency
70.300	RTTY calling frequency
70.350—70.400	Raynet
70.400—70.500	FM only
70.450	FM calling frequency

2 metre band

This is without a doubt the most popular amateur VHF band and signals can usually be heard on it in most areas at any time of day. The UK band extends from 144—146MHz but in other regions the band is extended even higher. Equipment for this band is relatively cheap and portable which makes it a favourite with amateurs for local contact work.

Range on the band varies enormously. Varying conditions can mean that a transmission of several hundred watts output may only be heard 20 or 30 miles away at one time, while a signal of a few watts could be picked up hundreds of miles away at another time. Peak progagation tends to be in the summer when sporadic-E activity is at its highest. The band is used for a whole range of transmission types and several modes are used. Frequency allocation, listed in Table 7.14, is more by a sort of gentlemen's agreement than anything else. The band is organised into blocks of transmission types.

The abbreviation 'ms', used in Table 7.14, stands for 'meteor scatter', a method of bouncing a radio signal off the tail of a meteor or a meteor shower. A similar method of communication is involved in 'moon-bounce'. These types of communications are generally beyond the scope of scanner users as highly sensitive equipment and massive aerial arrays are required.

Table 7.14 UK frequency allocations on the 2 metre band

Block type	Frequency (MHz)	Allocation
	144.000	
	144.000—144.015	Moonbounce
CW only	144.050	CW calling
	144.100	CW ms reference
	144.150	
SSB/CW only	144.250	GB2RS slow CW
	144.260	Raynet
	144.300	SSB calling
	144.400	SSB ms reference
	144.500	
All modes	144.500	SSTV calling
	144.540	Forbidden use
	144.600	RTTY calling
	144.675	Data calling
	144.700	FAX calling
	144.750	ATV calling
	144.775	Raynet
	144.800	Raynet
	144.825	Raynet
	144.845	
Beacons only		
	144.990	
Repeater inputs	145.000	R0
	145.025	R1
	145.050	R2
	145.075	R3

Table 7.14   *continued*

Block type	Frequency (MHz)	Allocation
	145.100	R4
	145.125	R5
	145.150	R6
	145.175	R7
	145.200	
FM Simplex	145.200	S8
channels	145.225	S9
	145.250	S10
	145.275	S11
	145.300	S12 RTTY/AFSK
	145.325	S13
	145.350	S14
	145.375	S15
	145.400	S16
	145.425	S17
	145.450	S18
	145.475	S19
	145.500	S20 calling
	145.525	S21 GB2RS News
	145.550	S22 Talk-in
	145.575	S23
	145.600	
Repeater output	145.600	R0
	145.625	R1
	145.650	R2
	145.675	R3
	145.700	R4
	145.725	R5
	145.750	R6
	145.775	R7
	145.800	
Satellite working only		
	146.000	

70 centimetre band

This band is allocated between 432.00 and 440MHz. It is allocated on a 'secondary' basis which means that amateurs using it must not interfere with other services on the band. The other services are mainly navigational positioning beacons known as 'SYLEDIS'.

The characteristics of the band are very similar to those of the 2 metre band with the exception that operators do not get the extreme ranges achieved at times on the 2 metre band. By and large the band is less used than the 2 metre band although in densely populated areas there can be a fairly high level of activity. As equipment for the band comes down in price, which it is doing, occupancy is likely to increase as many amateurs see the band as a means of escaping from the crowded 2 metre band.

Like the 2 metre band, the 70 centimetre band also has repeaters, throughout the country, which considerably increase the range of operation.

Frequency allocations, again divided into blocks of transmission types, is listed in Table 7.15.

Table 7.15 UK frequency allocations on the 70 centimetre band

Block type	Frequency (MHz)	Allocation
	432.000	
CW only	432.000—432.015	Moonbounce
	432.050	CW calling
	432.150	
SSB/CW only	432.200	UK SSB calling
	432.300	IARU SSB calling
	432.500	
Modes	432.600	RTTY working
	432.600	RTTY calling
	432.675	Data calling
	432.700	FAX calling
	432.800	
Beacons		
	433.000	
Repeater outputs	433.000	RB0
	433.025	RB1
	433.050	RB2
	433.075	RB3
	433.100	RB4
	433.125	RB5

Table 7.15   *continued*

Block type	Frequency (MHz)	Allocation
	433.150	RB6
	433.175	RB7
	433.200	RB8/SU8 Raynet
	433.225	RB9
	433.250	RB10
	433.275	RB11
	433.300	RB12/SU12 + RTTY
	433.325	RB13
	433.350	RB14
	433.375	
FM simplex	433.375	SU15
channels	433.400	SU16
	433.425	SU17
	433.450	SU18
	433.475	SU19
	433.500	SU20 FM calling
	434.600	
Repeater outputs	434.600	RB0
	434.625	RB1
	434.650	RB2
	434.675	RB3
	434.700	RB4
	434.725	RB5
	434.750	RB6
	434.775	RB7
	434.800	RB8
	434.825	RB9
	434.850	RB10
	434.875	RB11
	434.900	RB12 + RTTY
	434.925	RB13
	434.950	RB14
	435.500	
	434.000—440.000	Devoted to amateur Fast Scan Television where there is no interference to other allocated users.
	435.000—438.000	Amateur satellite service.
	440.000	

Land mobile services

Under the banner of land mobile services is a varied range of communications users. In the following section you will find listed private mobile radio, emergency services, message handling and paging.

The term 'land mobile' applies to any radio communications that takes place between either mobile-to-mobile or mobile-to-base, across land as opposed to air or marine. The mobile can either be a vehicle installation or a portable transceiver of the walkie-talkie type.

Ranges of such equipment vary enormously. In open country ranges of 20 or 30 miles are not unusual but in built-up areas this may be cut to considerably less. Users of mobile radio equipment operating in towns and cities often use aerials on very high buildings well away from the actual point of operation. Connection between the operator and the remote aerial site is usually through a private telephone line. Emergency services may have even more sophisticated arrangements with several aerial/transmitter sites to give total coverage of an area. This becomes particularly important when communication is to and from low powered handsets with limited aerial facilities.

Private mobile radio (PMR)

Private mobile radio is a form of communication between a base station and one or more mobile or portable units. Typical examples are the transceivers used by taxi firms. PMR is not to be confused with the government allocations, emergency services or car radiophones, all of which fall into different categories and are listed elsewhere.

Communication in the PMR bands can be either FM or AM and may be split frequency, or single frequency simplex. Only one band, VHF band 3 is available for duplex working.

Table 7.16 shows all bands allocated to PMR communications, listing them with respect to frequency and service allocations.

Public radiophones

Radiophones, also known as carphones, form part of a radio communications system that is connected to the normal telephone exchange at the base station. It allows a telephone type handset to be installed in a vehicle capable of making or receiving telephone calls. The service only operates in major towns and cities. It has the disadvantage of limited range and is being replaced by a cellular radio telephone system which relies on a whole network of base stations. The 'cellphone' system is computer-controlled and as the vehicle moves out of range of one base station it is automatically switched to the frequency of the next closest cell. The VHF radiophone service is half-duplex but the UHF cellular service is fully duplex.

Both services are FM only and can handle data as well as voice communications. Table 7.17 lists the allocated frequencies of the VHF radiophone band, while Table 7.18 lists those of the UHF cellular band.

Table 7.16 UK private mobile radio bands and frequency allocations

---

Band: VHF low (12.5kHz channel spacing)

Frequency (MHz)	Allocation
71.5125—72.7875	Mobile Tx
76.9625—77.5000	Mobile Tx
85.0125—86.2875	Base Tx
86.9625—87.5000	Base Tx
86.3000—86.7000	Single Simplex

COMMENT: Split frequency simplex separation usually either 10MHz or 13.5MHz

---

Band: VHF mid (12.5kHz channel spacing)

Frequency (MHz)	Allocation
105.00626—107.89375	Base Tx
138.00625—140.99375	Mobile Tx

COMMENT: Split frequency separation usually 33MHz. This band will be phased out by the end of 1995 to make way for FM broadcasting.

Band: VHF high (12.5kHz channel spacing)

Frequency (MHz)	Allocation
165.0625—168.2500	Base Tx
169.8625—173.0500	Mobile Tx
168.9500—169.8500	Single simplex

COMMENT: Split frequency separation usually 4.8MHz

Table 7.16   *continued*

Band: VHF band 3 (12.5kHz channel spacing)

Frequency (MHz)	Allocation
184.50—191.50	Mobile Tx
192.50—199.50	Mobile Tx
216.50—223.50	Mobile Tx
176.50—183.50	Base Tx
200.50—207.50	Base Tx
208.50—215.50	Base Tx
174.00—176.50	Single simplex
183.50—184.50	Single simplex
191.50—192.50	Single simplex
199.50—200.50	Single simplex
207.50—208.50	Single simplex
215.50—216.50	Single simplex
223.50—225.00	Single simplex

COMMENT: All these allocations are new and provisional so it is unlikely they will be in full use for some years. Split frequency separation will be 8.0MHz.

Band: UHF band (12.5kHz channel spacing)

Frequency (MHz)	Allocation
425.025—425.475	Mobile Tx
425.525—428.975	
445.525—445.975	Base Tx
440.025—443.475	
446.025—446.475	Single simplex

COMMENT: Split frequency separation either 14.5MHz or 20.5MHz.

Band: UHF London (12.5kHz channel spacing)

Frequency (MHz)	Allocation
431.00625—431.99375	Mobile Tx
448.00625—448.99375	Base Tx

COMMENT: This band is only available in the London area. Split frequency separation is 17MHz

Table 7.17 VHF radiophone band allocated frequencies (12.5kHz channel spacing — 4.5MHz separation)

Frequency (MHz)	Allocation
158.53125—159.9125	Mobile Tx
163.0375—164.4250	Base Tx

Table 7.18 UHF cellular band allocated frequencies (25kHz channel spacing — 45.0MHz separation)

Frequency (MHz)	Allocation
890.0125—904.9875	Mobile Tx
935.0125—949.9875	Base Tx

Telepoint

Telepoint is a cordless telephone system that does not confine the user to the usual 25-30 Metre radius of their own home. Telepoint terminals are set up at locations where there is a large movement of people such as high streets, railway stations and airports. The caller then uses his or her own small handset to dial in the normal way and the calls are connected through the public telephone exchange system. It is a little like cellular except the range is restricted to within a short distance of the telepoint terminal which is already being dubbed as a 'phone-zone'. The system works using relatively inexpensive and very compact handsets and at least one manufacturer will be selling a unit which can be used in the home as a normal cordless telephone.

Telepoint, also known as system CT2, uses single channel duplex and achieves this unusual method of operation by using digitally encoded speech (very similar to the principles used in a compact disc). This also has the added advantage that conversations cannot be overheard on normal radio equipment.

Table 7.18b Telepoint (system CT2)

Frequency	Allocation
864.0000—868.0000	Single channel duplex

COMMENT: 40 channels at 100kHz spacing using digitally encoded speech and FSK.

Wide area paging

This service provides for one way transmissions from a base station to a small pocket receiver. The transmission is coded to activate only the required pager. The simplest form of pagers merely emit a bleeping sound to alert the holder that they are wanted. Some of the more sophisticated types can receive a short digital message that appears on a small liquid crystal display. Wide area pagers usually cover a specific area such as a town but one service, run by British Telecom, covers most of the country. Wide area paging should not be confused with 'on-site' paging.

Table 7.19 lists wide area paging allocated frequencies

Table 7.19 Wide area paging allocated frequencies

Band	Frequency (MHz)
VHF (12.5kHz spacing)	153.025—153.475
UHF (25kHz spacing)	454.0125—454.825

On-site paging

Similar to wide area paging but low powered and operating over a small area such as a factory, building site, etc. Sometimes the pager has a small and simple transmitter which allows the user to acknowledge that the paging signal has been received. AM or FM modes may be transmitted, and data communications are possible.

Table 7.20 lists on-site paging allocated frequencies and services. At VHF a 12.5kHz channel spacing is used, at UHF 25kHz.

Table 7.20 On-site paging allocated frequencies

Band	Frequency (MHz)	Allocation
VHF	26.957—27.283	Private paging
	31.725—31.775	Hospital paging
	161.000—161.100	(acknowledge)
UHF	459.100—459.500	Private paging

Message handling

Many smaller companies may not be able to justify the cost of their own radio-telephone network and so, instead, may make use of a message handling service in which messages are verbally passed between mobile and portable transceivers, through a central contractor. Some message handling services work in a restricted area such as a town or city, but some do span most of the country by using base stations in strategic places.

Table 7.21 lists allocated frequencies for message handling services.

Table 7.21 Message handling services' allocated frequencies

Frequency (MHz)	Allocation
157.4500—158.4000	Mobile Tx
159.9375—160.5375	
162.0500—163.0000	
164.4375—165.0375	Base Tx

Land emergency services

Land emergency services are normally police, fire and ambulance services. Some services are also found on bands allocated to PMR but nearly all police forces operate in bands allocated to the UK Home Office. In addition to the bands listed in Table 7.22, some emergency services in some areas may be located in government mobile allocations (see Tables 7.1 and 7.2). Note that, in accordance with international agreements, the allocation between 97.60 and 102.10MHz is being re-allocated for broadcast use. Some services have already moved off this band and others will do so over the next few years.

Table 7.22 Land emergency services' band and allocated frequencies

Band: VHF low (12.5kHz channel spacing, AM) Frequency (MHz)	Allocation
70.5000—71.5000	Fire bases
81.9000—83.9000	Fire mobiles

Table 7.22   *continued*

Band: VHF mid (12.5kHz channel spacing, FM)
Frequency (MHz)   *Allocation*

80.00—84.00	Mobile Tx
97.60—102.10	Base Tx

Band: VHF high (12.5kHz channel spacing, AM/FM)

Frequency (MHz)	*Allocation*
143.00—144.0000	Mobile Tx
152.00—153.0000	Base Tx
147.2000—148.0000	Mobile Tx
155.2000—156.0000	Base Tx
146.0000—147.2000	Fixed links
166.2750—166.5250	Ambulances

Band: UHF low (12.5kHz channel spacing, FM)

Frequency (MHz)	*Allocation*
420.00—425.00	
429.00—432.00	
443.50—445.00	
446.00—450.00	
451.000—453.000	
459.50—470.00	
464.9000—467.0000	

Band: UHF high (25 kHz channel spacing, FM)

Frequency (MHz)	*Allocation*
862.00—864.00	

COMMENT: Usually split frequency simplex but channel pairings vary.

Citizens' band radio

Citizens' band radio communications originated in the USA where it was felt there was a need for a low powered, short distance communication system. The idea was for a low cost service with the minimum of regulations where the user did not have to comply with strict licensing conditions to prove an essential use for two-way radio. Originally it was to give such people as small businesses, servicemen, truckers, farmers and social organisations as a means of communications.

Later, CB acquired a cult following and a colourful slang language all of its own. These days it bears little resemblance to its original aims.

Legal and illegal

The UK started off with an illegal CB service using the same channel allocations as those in the USA. AM equipment, designed for America, was smuggled into Britain. CB became such a craze that thousands of illegal transceivers were in use and often caused havoc to legitimate users of the frequencies which included radio modellers, paging systems and meteorological equipment. Finally, the Government, which appeared reluctant to establish a legal service, gave in. The service introduced in November 1981 had slightly different frequencies to the American equipment and used frequency modulation.

Britain has three CB allocations, two at HF the other at UHF (see Table 7.23). Even so, American equipment, still illegal in the UK, is used from time to time, particularly when conditions favour long distance contact. The UHF allocation tends not to attract many users because of the high cost of the equipment involved. Aerial systems are also more critical and costly at these frequencies.

The band is to be withdrawn but a date has yet to be fixed.

Range

Across open country usable HF ranges of up to 20 or more miles can be expected but a lot will depend on circumstances, ie, base/base, base/ mobile or mobile/mobile working. Ranges are considerably reduced in built-up areas but under lift conditions ranges may become almost global. The band is very prone to the effects of the 11 year sunspot cycle (which will start to lift again around 1987). When that happens it should not be unusual to hear transmissions from the USA, Australia, Asia, South America, etc.

On the UHF band, activity is usually limited to local conditions, but even at these high frequencies lift conditions do occur. For instance, cross channel contacts between stations in southern England and the Channel Islands (distances of more than 100 miles) regularly take place in the summer months.

Note that HF ranges quoted are only likely to be achieved by using a proper CB aerial. Most discone-type aerials, favoured for scanner operation, operate quite poorly at lower frequencies. The same, in fact, goes for UHF ranges, where an ordinary discone cannot compete with a multi-element Yagi pointed at the transmitting station.

Table 7.23 UK (and USA) CB channels and allocated frequencies

Channel	Frequencies (MHz)		
	UK/HF (FM)	UK/UHF (FM)	CEPT (FM)
01	27.60125	934.01	26.965
02	27.61125	934.06	26.975
03	27.62125	934.11	26.985
04	27.63125	934.16	27.005
05	27.64125	934.21	27.015
06	27.65125	934.26	27.025
07	27.66125	934.31	27.035
08	27.67125	934.36	27.055
09	27.68125	934.41	27.065
10	27.69125	934.46	27.075
11	27.70125	934.51	27.085
12	27.71125	934.56	27.105
13	27.72125	934.61	27.115
14	27.73125	934.66	27.125
15	27.74125	934.71	27.135
16	27.75125	934.76	27.155
17	27.76125	934.81	27.165
18	27.77125	934.86	27.175
19	27.78125	934.91	27.185
20	27.79125	934.96	27.205
21	27.80125		27.215
22	27.81125		27.225
23	27.82125		27.255
24	27.83125		27.235
25	27.84125		27.245
26	27.85125		27.265
27	27.86125		27.275
28	27.87125		27.285
29	27.88125		27.295
30	27.89125		27.305
31	27.90125		27.315
32	27.91125		27.325
33	27.92125		27.335
34	27.93125		27.345
35	27.94125		27.355
36	27.95125		27.365
37	27.96125		27.375
38	27.97125		27.385
39	27.98125		27.395
40	27.99125		27.405

Space satellites

Even old hands at scanning, like myself, still get a kick out of hearing signals from space — even if they are not voice transmissions. For that reason I have included here a wide range of frequency allocations which should enable scanner users to pick up at least some signals.

A large amount of hardware now circles the earth in the form of man-made satellites. Some of these devices stay permanently in space (communication, weather and navigation vehicles); others, such as the American space shuttle, only stay up for a pre-determined period. The latter are usually manned with crews; astronauts in the case of the Americans, cosmonauts in the case of the Russians.

For the scanner user, not all forms of transmission can be received from these space vehicles as many of the frequencies used are in the SHF band (3—30GHz). However *some* VHF and UHF frequencies are used and those likely to be of interest to scanner users are some of the voice communications for the astronauts/cosmonauts, amateur communications relays and weather satellites. The latter transmit pictures back to earth in digital form which, unfortunately, means the received signal cannot just be fed straight into a television set. However, some home computers can be used with suitable software programs to convert the signals into a picture.

Various other transmissions

Many of the 'space' allocations shown in Tables 7.1 and 7.2 do not contain transmissions of interest. Many satellites transmit streams of data from on-board sensors, used for a variety of scientific measurements, and without suitable decoding equipment these signals are meaningless. The same is true of satellites used for navigation purposes. Also, most of the communications and television satellites, both for relay and broadcasting, operate at frequencies well removed from the coverage of most scanners.

Satellite reception problems

By the time satellite transmissions reach earth they are very weak. In some instances it is necessary to use special aerials to receive the signals. Remembering the comments in Chapter 5 about aerials and polarisation, one problem in the reception of an orbiting satellite's transmissions is that, as the satellite moves, its aerial effectively changes polarity in relation to the aerial of the ground station, causing the received signal to, apparently, fade away and then come back again, every few minutes. This can be overcome, though, by using a crossed dipole aerial and, again, you should refer to Chapter 5 for more details.

Movement of the space craft also causes an effect, known as doppler shift, which slightly alters the received frequency of the radio signal.

This can be a nuisance as it means a scanner must be tuned off the centre frequency to track the shifting signal. On some scanners, such as the Yaesu, AOR-2002 and Icom, this presents no great problem as, fortunately, the manual tuning control can be used to track the signal. On the AOR-2001 and similar scanners it may be possible to completely overcome the effect by switching to wide FM reception mode, although this will not work if other signals are present on adjacent channels.

Amateur satellites

Amateur satellite transmissions are among some of the easiest to receive as the satellites are designed to transmit on frequencies that are easily picked up by unsophisticated equipment. Two satellites that can be received with just a simple aerial are UOSATs 1 & 2, on 145.825MHz. The satellites were built by amateurs at the University of Surrey and, although they are mostly used for sending down data in ASCII computer code, they also have an interesting on-board synthesiser. This can be heard as a robot-type voice listing strings of numbers.

UOSAT transmissions might not be very exciting but they do make a good starting point to get the feel of satellite reception. Aerial phasing and doppler shift problems will all become apparent. Bear in mind that UOSATs are orbiting satellites and so transmissions can only be received for a few minutes at a time unless sophisticated trackable beam aerials are used to follow them from horizon to horizon. Occasionally their orbits take them well away from the UK and, at such times, it might not be possible to receive transmissions at all. In addition to their VHF transmission they also transmit signals on UHF, but in the author's experience these are much more difficult to receive.

Amateur communications satellite transmissions are more interesting but they are also harder to receive. It is necessary to, at least, use a set of crossed dipoles, if not a Yagi aerial, with motors to control direction and elevation.

The way communications take place using these communications satellites is that an amateur transmits up to the satellite on an 'uplink' frequency. The satellite then re-transmits the signal back on a different, 'downlink', frequency. In this way it is quite easy to span large distances using VHF and UHF: communications between Europe and the Americas are quite normal.

This method of re-transmitting the signal is known as 'transponding'. The UOSATs do not have transponders as they are experimental scientific satellites and their job is merely to transmit data from on-board sensors.

Table 7.24 Amateur satellites

Vehicle	Beacon	Mode	uplinks	downlinks
RS 5	29.330 29.450	A	145.910—145.950	29.410—29.450
RS 7	29.340 29.501	A	145.960—146.000	29.460—29.500
RS 10/11	29.357 29.403 29.407 29.453	K T A KT	21.600—21.200 21.600—21.200 145.860—145.900 21.160—21.200	29.360—29.400 145.860—145.900 29.360—29.400 all above
Oscar 9 (UOSAT 1)	145.825 435.025		ASCII or "digitalker"	
Oscar 10	145.810 145.987	B	436.150—436.950	145.830—145.970
Oscar 11 (UOSAT 2)	145.826 435.025			
Oscar 12	435.797 435.913			
Oscar 13	145.812	B	435.439—435.576	145.823—145.960
Mir (licensed cosmonauts only)			143.625	143.625
FO12 (Fuji)	453.797 453.913		Switched off for long periods	

Table 7.24 lists amateur satellites, together with allocated frequencies. With the exception of Oscar 10, all of the satellites are standard orbiting types. Oscar 10 operates in an elliptical orbit which means that it may remain in range for several hours. The RS series are Russian-built while the others have been made by the voluntary organisation, AMSAT.

The frequencies of most interest to scanner users are the downlink ones, but it should be noted that often some, if not all, of the satellites are in orbits that are out of UK range, and satellites are occasionally switched off for long periods, to allow for such things as battery charging from their solar panels.

Some of the RS series satellites are coming to the end of their useful life and Oscar 10 is out of control.

Weather satellites

Most people will be familiar with weather satellite pictures now commonly used during television weather forecasts. These pictures are transmitted from satellites in a coded fashion: circuits in the satellite break the picture up into small segments which are then transmitted as a stream of audio tones. Upon reception at the ground station, these tones must be decoded and segments re-assembled back into a picture. Sophisticated receiving equipment is available for the job, but it is possible to use a home computer to get very acceptable results for a fraction of the price.

At least two companies in the UK, Timestep Electronics and Halbar, can supply software for the BBC-B computer for weather picture decoding and assembly. However, it should be noted that although these signals are quite easy to receive, they are fairly wide band and computer pictures will only be possible with a scanner that has an intermediate frequency bandwidth of at least 30kHz in FM mode. Scanners such as the AORs, Yaesu and Icom are suitable. For anyone with the technical knowledge it is not too difficult to change the IF filters on any scanner to achieve wider bandwidth.

Table 7.25 Weather satellites

Satellite	Frequency	Origin
Cosmos 1766	137.400	USSR
Cosmos 1869	137.400	USSR
Meteor 2/15	137.850	USSR
Meteor 2/16	137.400	USSR
Meteor 2/17	137.300	USSR
Meteor 3/1	137.850	USSR
Meteor 3/2	137.850	USSR
Meteor 30	136.970	USSR
NOAA 10	137.500	USA
NOAA 11	137.620	USA
Meteosat 3	1691.00	Geostationary Ch.2 (High resolution digital)
Meteosat 3	1694.50	Geostationary Ch.1 (Low resolution WEFAX)
Meteosat 4		To be announced in June 1989

Details of weather satellites are listed in Table 7.25, even though the average scanner user will not have facilities to convert them into pictures. Most scanner users will find the details useful if only to check that they can receive signals direct from space. Several weather satellites can be heard in the 137MHz band, but it should be noted that they are only switched on at certain times.

Table 7.26 Miscellaneous satellites

Satellite	Frequency	Details
NASA Shuttles	259.700	AM voice
	270.000	AM voice
	296.800	AM voice
Mir (USSR)	142.400	FM voice
	143.625	FM voice
	166.140	Robot/beacon
Soyuz supply modules	121.750	FM voice
Navigation beacons	149.000—150.050 Cicada	
	399.000—400.050 Transit	
Military comms	235.000—273.000	
	FleetSatcoms, etc (some FM)	

Miscellaneous satellites

A look at the frequency allocations in Tables 7.1 and 7.2 shows that several bands are allocated for space and satellite operation. Many of these bands have little, if any, activity and in recent years as technology has progressed, space communications have tended to move to higher frequencies — usually of several thousand megahertz. Even so, there is occasionally voice traffic in some of the VHF bands and a list of typical users is given in Table 7.26. Do note, though, that they might not always carry transmissions. For instance two frequencies are shown for the NASA space shuttle but on any one flight this band might never be used. Keen space communications fans know that this side of the hobby often means much patience. If at first you hear nothing, try, try and try again.

In the two very narrow navigation satellite bands shown in Table 7.26 it will occasionally be possible to hear either the Russian 'CICADA' system or the USA's 'TRANSIT' service. In the UK reception of 'CICADA' signal transmissions is usually possible several times a day. They are AM signals sounding like fast morse code.

8 RT procedure

English is the most internationally accepted language in radio communications, yet many communicators appear to have a language all of their own. There is a good reason for some of the codes, abbreviations and expressions that are used on the air: so that misunderstandings can be avoided. The use of a set of common expressions means that even people who speak different languages can make and receive basic messages correctly. In some cases, however (CB being a good example), the expressions used are just part of the folklore which goes with the medium.

We shall first consider some things that are common to most operators.

Phonetic alphabet

Sometimes, under difficult conditions, it may be impossible to tell what the user transmitting from another station is saying. Under such circumstances it is usual to spell out the message, coding the letters as words, using the 'phonetic alphabet':

A Alpha	N November
B Bravo	O Oscar
C Charlie	P Papa
D Delta	Q Quebec
E Echo	R Roger
F Foxtrot	S Sierra
G Golf	T Tango
H Hotel	U Uniform
I India	V Victor
J Juliet	W Whisky
K Kilo	X X-ray
L Lima	Y Yankee
M Mike	Z Zulu

These phonetics are widely used in callsigns. For instance, amateur station G7XYZ would be Golf Seven X-Ray Yankee Zulu. Similar use of phonetics will be heard in aircraft callsigns which are usually made up of a string of letters with the first or first two letters, denoting the country of registration.

Some expressions are common to most radio users:

Roger An almost universal expression meaning 'I understand or acknowledge receipt of your message'.

Wilco Not quite as common as *Roger*. It means I will comply with your instructions.

Copy A message or part of it. For instance, the expression 'I copy you' means I am able to understand you, I hear you.

Mayday The international call of distress. The word is repeated three times and means that an emergency situation has occurred. All stations on the frequency, except that calling *Mayday* and that providing assistance, must observe strict radio silence.

Pan-Pan A call indicating that assistance is required urgently but no one is in immediate danger.

Affirmative Means yes.

Negative Means no.

Time

Even within the relatively close confines of Europe many countries may be in different time zones and so a standard time system has been adopted so that complex calculations can be avoided during radio communications. Universal Time Constant (UTC) is the same time as measured at Greenwich (previously known as GMT).

Occasionally, some radio operators will refer to UTC as 'Zulu', eg, '1500 hours Zulu' is 3 o'clock in the afternoon. British summer time (BST) is known as 'Alpha', that is, UTC + 1 hour. Virtually all radio traffic references to time are made using the 24 hour clock system.

Amateurs

Amateurs form one of only two groups of radio users (the other is CB) who usually 'transmit blind': that is they put out calls for contact with anyone who happens to be on the same frequency or channel. Professional users, on the other hand, except in emergencies, only put out calls for specific stations. But amateurs, too, might well call up particular stations. And, even when transmitting blind, they may well specify that they only want contacts into a certain area. For instance, it is not unusual under lift conditions to hear UK amateurs calling for contacts on the Continent or even from a specific country. While most amateurs will happily chat to anyone who happens to be on the air many will, at times, only want to work long distances. One of the attractions of the hobby is being able, on occasions, to work not only far flung places but also small countries where there may only be a few amateurs. Such 'catches' are a little bit like a stamp collector finding a rare stamp.

Amateurs use expressions known as 'Q-codes' to abbreviate messages. Some typical Q-codes follow. Note that most can be either a statement or a question, eg, QRP can mean 'shall I reduce my power?' or 'reduce your power', depending on the context of use.

International Q-codes

QRA Name of station. Sometimes you may hear the expression 'QRA locator'. This is a grid system used by amateurs to work out the distances between each other.

QRM Interference. This is 'man-made', such as noise from electrical equipment.

QRN Interference. Natural interference, such as static.

QRP Reducing transmitter power. The expression 'QRP station' means a transmitter that is always operated at very low power. Some amateurs specialise in this kind of operation.

QRT Stop sending/transmitting. A station saying "I am going QRT' usually means he is closing down.

QRZ Who is calling?

QSB Signals fading.

QSK Can I break in on your contact. Often a query from a station wanting to join in a 'net', that is, a group of amateurs passing conversation back and forth.

QSL Acknowledge receipt.

QSO Communicate or communication. For example 'I had a QSO with a French station'.

QSY Change frequency or channel. For example 'Let us QSY to 144.310MHz'.

QTH Strictly speaking the position of the station in terms of latitude and longitude. Often used, though, to simply refer to wherever the station is by naming the town, village, etc.

There are many other Q-codes but they are rarely used by amateurs using speech for communications.

Reporting codes

Amateurs, like other radio users, have a system of reporting on the signal that they receive. The other station will usually find this information useful as it can tell him what propagation conditions are like and if his equipment is performing correctly. Unlike most scanners, amateur radio transceivers usually have a signal strength meter to indicate received signal strength. The lower part of the scale is usually marked from 0 to 9, above this the scale is marked in decibels (dB). The internationally recognised method of reporting on signals is known as the 'RST code': R is readability, S is signal strength and T is tone. For speech communication the T is not used as it applies only to morse code.

Amateurs will usually be heard to say something like 'you are four by seven'. That means readability 4, signal strength 7.

The code follows:

Readability
R1 Unreadable
R2 Barely readable
R3 Readable with considerable difficulty
R4 Readable with practically no difficulty
R5 Perfectly readable

Signal strength
S1 Faint, barely perceptible
S2 Very weak
S3 Weak
S4 Fair
S5 Fairly good
S6 Good
S7 Moderately strong
S8 Strong
S9 Extremely strong
S9-
+ Meter needle on the end of the scale

The last one is an unofficial code but often used and a corresponding measurement may be given in decibels, eg, 'You are 20dB over 9'.

Call sign prefixes

It is possible to identify the country from which a station is transmitting by the first few letters and/or numbers of the callsign. Table 8.1 lists typical countries whose stations may be heard in the UK under some lift conditions.

Contest stations

Occasionally you may hear contests in operation. Participating stations, operated by an individual or a group, are required to make as many

Table 8.1 Amateur callsign prefixes, with associated countries

Prefix	Country	Prefix	Country
C31	Andorra	OE	Austria
CN	Morocco	OH	Finland
CT1,4	Portugal	OHO	Aaland Island
CT2	Azores	OJO	Market Reef
DA,DL	F.R. Germany	OK,OL	Czechoslovakia
DM,Y2-9	D.R. Germany	ON	Belgium
EA	Spain	OY	Faroe Island
EA6	Balearic Isle	OZ	Denmark
EA8	Canary Isle	PA-PI	Netherlands
EA9	Ceuta/Mellila	SK,SM	Sweden
EI,EJ	Eire	SV	Greece
EL	Liberia	SV9	Crete
F	France	TA	Turkey
FC	Corsica	TF	Iceland
G	England	UA	USSR
GD	Isle of Man	UB5,UT5	Ukraine
GI	N. Ireland		
GJ	Jersey (CI)	UP2	Lithuania
GM	Scotland	UQ2	Latvia
GU	Guernsey (CI)	UR2	Estonia
GW	Wales	YO	Rumania
HA,HG	Hungary	YU,YT	Yugoslavia
HB	Switzerland	ZB2	Gibraltar
HBO	Leichtenstein	3A	Monaco
HV	Vatican City	3V8	Tunisia
I	Italy	4UI	United Nations
LA,LB	Norway	7X	Algeria
LX	Luxembourg	9A	San Marino
LZ	Bulgaria	9H	Malta

contacts as possible within a given space of time. The biggest such contest in the UK is the VHF National Field Day (NFD) organised by the Radio Society of Great Britain, which takes place every year on the first week-end in July between 3.00pm on the Saturday and 3.00pm on the Sunday. During the event the whole spectrum around 144.300MHz comes alive with thousands of transmitting stations. Unfortunately, most of the transmissions are SSB so will only be of interest to owners of more expensive scanners. However, for such owners this event usually provides an occasion to hear a lot of long distance stations. Lift conditions are normally good at this time of year and many continental stations beam their transmission towards the UK to take part in the contest.

Special event stations

Occasionally you may hear 'special event stations' which are usually operated by a group of amateurs such as an amateur radio club. They are granted a special one-off callsign to celebrate special events such as a country fair. Callsigns are often granted to have some significance to the event. For instance, amateurs operating from the Totnes Agricultural Fair might use the callsign GB2TAF. The GB prefix is the normal one used for special event stations although during the Victory-in-Europe celebrations during 1985, the GV prefix was used in the callsigns of associated stations.

Repeaters

Details of how repeaters work were outlined in Chapter 2. Repeaters in the 2 metre and 70 centimetre bands operate in FM mode and so can be received on any scanner that covers the bands. They are recognised as a regular transmission of morse code containing the two letters which identify which repeater they are. Amateurs often call blind on repeaters and you may well hear the expression 'This is GUIDKD listening through WD'. That means that amateur station GUIDKD has accessed the repeater with callsign WD and is awaiting any replies.

Marine

The international VHF marine band as we saw in Chapter 7 is channelised. The standard procedure at commencement of any transmission on the band is to first put out a call on channel 16: the calling and distress channel, requesting contact with a particular station. When that station replies, both then move to a 'working channel'.

This method of operation means that at any time there are hundreds of stations listening to channel 16, and so if any boat or ship needs help someone is bound to hear the call. A further advantage is that it enables shore stations to make general broadcasts to ships informing them of weather information, safety warnings and lists of ships (traffic lists) for whom there are telephone link calls. These transmissions are not made on channel 16 but the shore station tells ships which channel or channels to move to.

Vessels licensed for marine RT are given a callsign comprising letters, numbers or both, depending on where the ship is registered. Generally the official callsign is only used, however, when establishing link calls. For other contacts the vessel will only usually give the ship or boat's name.

Photograph 8(a) A busy modern port needs radio communication to co-ordinate the movement and berthing of hundreds of trawlers, pleasure craft, ferries and cargo ships.

Securité

Pronounced 'securitay' this word, repeated three times, precedes any broadcast transmission where there is reference to safety. Again, broadcasts telling ships that there is a securité message will be broadcast on channel 16, will give the channel to move to for the details.

Securité broadcasts usually concern 'navigational warnings'. Typically they might inform vessels that a certain beacon or lighthouse is out of action, or they might warn of floating obstructions such as cargo washed off a ship's deck or a capsized vessel.

Some shore stations have the task of making regular broadcasts in busy shipping areas where there may be a need to pass frequent safety messages.Typical is Cherbourg Radio (channel 11) which transmits safety information every half hour for the southern part of the English Channel — possibly the busiest shipping zone in the world.

Weather

All coastal stations transmit regular weather forecasts and gale warnings. Again, forewarning of a weather forecast or gale warning will be made on channel 16 and the station will say which working channels will carry the forecast.

More localised forecasts are made by some ports, using the same procedure as the coastal station. Normally such forecasts are broadcast on the regular port operations channel.

Port operations

So far we have looked largely at the kind of transmissions and broadcasts that are from coastal stations covering a wide area. However, the marine VHF band is also used for other kinds of contact, in particular port operations. Many ports are busy places and some have traffic handling facilities almost as sophisticated as airports.

Typical radio traffic concerns departure and arrival of ships, ferries and pleasure craft. Port controllers, for example, may have to hold some ships off-shore until other ships have left and made space for them. They may be contacted by yachts wanting mooring spaces in marinas. Other tasks involve liaison with bodies such as customs and immigration officers.

Ship-to-ship

Several channels are set aside for ship-to-ship use. These are used for a variety of purposes: anything from the local yacht club marshalling a dinghy race to trawlermen discussing where the best catches are.

Emergencies

Britain has probably the best marine emergency services in the world; its tradition as a seafaring nation is probably responsible for this. The waters around the British Isles are covered by lifeboat and coastguard stations, and back-up to these services comes from the Air Force and Royal Navy. All services are on call to assist with emergencies at sea.

The first warning of an emergency will come with a Mayday call. This is internationally recognised and will be made on channel 16. Normally, a coastal station or port will receive the call and put the emergency services into action. Where coastal stations are out of range, a ship may well respond to the Mayday. During this time all traffic, other than emergency traffic, is supposed to cease on channel 16. It is sad, however, that some radio operators ignore this and it is not unusual for the emergency services to have their messages jammed by ship's operators who appear to consider their own relatively trivial messages more important than other people's lives.

No two emergencies are the same. In some instances it may just be a small vessel lost in fog and worried about running onto rocks. In such cases coastal stations might be able to offer position fixes by taking bearings on the transmissions of the vessel in distress pinpointing the vessel's position.

At the other end of the scale, the emergency might be a ship sinking in a storm. The crew may have abandoned the vessel and be in the water or on liferafts. On these occasions all emergency services may be involved. An RNLI lifeboat may be on the scene, helicopters from the nearest naval station sweeping the sea for survivors and overhead an RAF coastal command Nimrod with its massively powerful search-lights lighting up the area. It's also quite likely that other ships in the area may come to the scene to assist.

All this requires communications if the efforts of all services are to be co-ordinated. While the coastal station will act as the main co-ordination centre, at the scene of the rescue the various groups involved will need to communicate, too. In UK waters, the lifeboat remains in contact with the coastal station on channel 0 — the helicopters and aircraft will probably be on this channel as well. Normal commercial vessels are *not* permitted to use this channel so they will stay on channel 16. The coastal station and lifeboat may therefore have to work both channels. Some lifeboats and coastguard vessels are fitted with aircraft band equipment to provide communications on the airband search and rescue and emergency frequencies (see Chapter 7).

Communications on the marine bands are, by and large, carried out in plain language. The few expressions and procedures described are the only likely exceptions.

Aviation

The world of aviation is the winner when we come to judge it in terms of the number of expressions and jargon. However, little of it is trivial. Aircraft crew cope with a variety of complex situations and may well be flying in and out of countries where air traffic controllers have little if any understanding of the English language.

Like the marine band the aircraft band is channelised, but the channels are referred to by their actual frequency and not by a channel number. The procedure for contacting a station is also very different. There is no common calling channel: a pilot wanting to call a ground station simply looks up the frequency and calls on it.

Callsigns

All civilian aircraft have a registration. In some instances this will consist solely of letters with the first letter or letters denoting the country of registration. In other instances, such as aircraft registered in the USA the registration may be a letter followed by numbers. Generally, privately owned light aircraft or those operated as air-taxis will use their registration as their radio callsign.

Normal procedure for making contact with the ground station will be to give the full callsign. The controller will reply, perhaps, referring to the aircraft by the full callsign, in which case the pilot will again, when transmitting, use the full callsign. At some stage though, for the sake of brevity, the approach controller will just use the last two letters and from then on the pilot will do the same.

Photograph 8(b) Typical radio station on a light aircraft. The radio console is the stack in the centre. From top to bottom: DME (distance measuring equipment), console selector (allows pilot to chose which radio output goes to his headset), Navcom one (communication frequency on the left window, for navigation on the right), NAVCOM 2, and transponder.

Larger aircraft, such as those used on regular passenger carrying routes, may use the same type of callsign, or a special callsign based on the airline's name and typically may also use the flight number for that service. Again the ground controller will probably, at some stage, abbreviate this and just use the number: from then on the aircrew will do the same.

Numbers preceded by the word 'Ascot' denote the callsign of a British military aircraft flying on a civilian route. The USAF equivalent is the pre-fix 'Mac'.

Landing instructions

First contact an aircraft has with an airfield is usually on the approach frequency. After transmitting on the frequency and identifying the aircraft, the pilot usually gives aircraft position and altitude. The approach controller then transmits information relating to airfield barometric pressure (QFE), the wind direction and speed, the runway in use (runways are always identified by the compass heading needed to land on them), and details of other aircraft in the landing pattern or about to take off. Temperature and visibility in kilometres may be also given. If the weather is bad the RVR (runway visual range) may be referred to. The pilot needs to know the QFE (sometimes just called the 'fox echo') so that the aircraft's altimeter may be set so that it will read zero feet at runway level. Other information such as runway state (if affected by rain, ice or snow) may be transmitted, followed by instructions to remain at present altitude or start descending to circuit height (often about 1000 feet). Some of this information the pilot will repeat back.

As the aircraft gets closer to the airport there will come a stage where the approach controller instructs the pilot to change to the tower frequency. The pilot always repeats the frequency to be changed to: this is standard procedure when changing frequency at any point in a flight.

Now the pilot calls the tower and again will give his position and altitude. The aircraft may be making a straight-in approach, that is, arriving at the airfield in line with the runway or he may be 'joining the circuit'. The circuit is an imaginary path around the airfield in the form of a racetrack. It can be in a lefthand or righthand direction and, once joined, the pilot will report at various stages such as downwind leg, base leg and finals. Finals occur at a given distance from the runway and the pilot will always tell the controller when the aircraft is one mile out. Throughout this stage of the flight the pilot will be given various instructions and updated QFE, wind speed and direction information. At any stage of the approach the pilot may be told to divert course because the controller cannot yet fit him in with other traffic. The instruction may be to briefly orbit over a given position, or to fly out further to a given point and then re-join the landing pattern.

Once on the ground the pilot may be told to change frequency yet again (particularly at larger airfields), this time to speak to the ground handler. Here, instructions on which taxiways to use and where to park the aircraft will be given.

SRA and PAR radar let-down

Occasionally, in bad visibility, a pilot may need to be 'talked-down'. SRA (surveillance radar approach) may be used to give the pilot precise instructions to reach the end of the runway. Normally, the airfield has a special frequency for this and once the pilot has established contact with the controller there is a point when the controller tells the pilot not to acknowledge further instructions. From then on, the controller gives the pilot a running commentary on the aircraft's position in relation to an imaginary line drawn outwards from the runway, known as the 'centre-line'. Compass headings may be given to the pilot, to steer the aircraft, in order to get on to the centre-line. Other information given tells the pilot how far the aircraft is from the runway and what height it should be at. At a point about half a mile from the runway, the controller announces that the approach is complete. If the pilot cannot see the runway at this stage the approach must be abandoned for another, or the aircraft is diverted to another airfield. Failing to touch-down results in a 'go-around' (formerly an 'overshoot').

PAR (precision radar approach) is similar, but also tells the pilot altitude and whether or not the aircraft is on the 'glide slope'.

Startup

The procedure at the start of a flight varies from airfield to airfield. On smaller airfields the pilot may start the aircraft and then ask for take-off instructions. The ground controller transmits details of which runway is in use, QFE and wind, then instructs the pilot to start taxiing to a holding point just before the end of the runway. Once the runway is clear, the controller allows the aircraft to take off and relays other instructions such as which height to climb to and when the aircraft can start turning on course.

At bigger airfields, particularly those in busy flight areas, the procedure may be far more complicated and will depend to some extent on whether the flight is VFR (visual flight rules) or IFR (instrument flight rules). The first, VFR, is where an aircraft flies solely by dead reckoning. In other words, the pilot navigates by using a compass and a map, looking out of the aircraft windows for landmarks. The second, IFR, is where the pilot uses radionavigation and instruments to cover the route. Most commercial flights are IFR and such flights are always along designated airways routes. Prior to a flight the pilot files a flight plan with Air Traffic Control which is telexed to controllers on the aircraft's route, who are then aware of the type of aircraft, altitude requested and destination.

At commencement of the flight the pilot informs the tower that all is ready. At this stage the controller may well only say the aircraft is clear to start up and, perhaps, will give the temperature. Once the pilot informs the controller the aircraft is ready for take-off, taxiing instructions, the QFE, the runway in use and the wind details are all given. At this stage or shortly after clearance is given to the pilot, detailing destination, the airways to use and altitudes. In the UK airways are identified by colours (red, blue, green, white, amber) with a number. After the actual take-off, the aircraft may be handed over to another controller, such as approach, before the pilot is finally told to contact 'airways' or 'information' services.

Airways

Busy air routes, such as those over Europe, are divided up into countries and regions which have central control points for all the air routes in the sectors. Although VFR flights at low altitudes can, by and large, choose the course they fly, this is not the case at higher altitudes in the airways. Now we are in the realm of 'controlled airspace' and pilots *must* fly along a certain course at a certain height. The airways are marked at regular points, and where they cross, by beacons on the ground. These are used for navigation purposes and also form what are known as 'compulsory

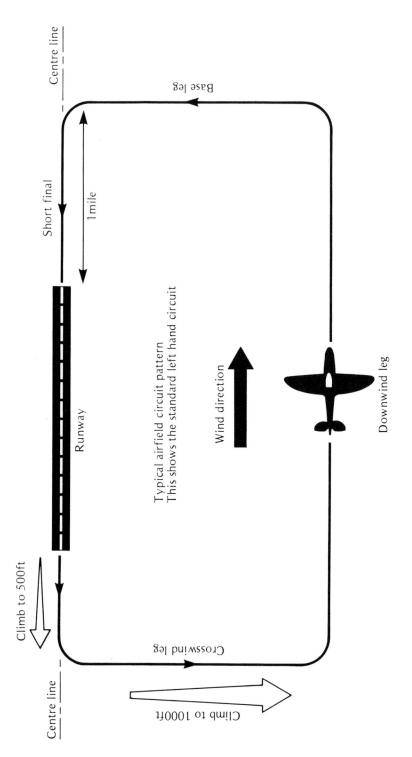

Centre line

Base leg

Short final

1mile

Runway

Typical airfield circuit pattern
This shows the standard left hand circuit

Wind direction

Downwind leg

Climb to 500ft

Crosswind leg

Centre line

Climb to 1000ft

reporting points': as the aircraft passes over a beacon the pilot must report to the sector controller, giving the name of the beacon, flight level (at higher altitudes the height is abbreviated, eg, 10,000 feet becomes 'flight level one-zero-zero'), and 'forward estimate' time for the next reporting point. These points are referred to by the name of the place where the beacon is sited.

Towards the end of the journey the pilot may be given a fairly complex set of instructions. Landing at major airports like London Heathrow may, at busy times, involve joining the 'stack': an imaginary spiral staircase in the sky. The aircraft joins at the top and flies a racetrack shaped circuit, slowly dropping to different flight levels until, at the bottom, it is routed to the airfield.

Flight information
Everything above 25,000 feet is 'controlled airspace' (in some regions airspace below that altitude is controlled, too). Pilots can obtain details of traffic movements in the region from the UIR (upper-flight information region) service. Below that level, information is provided by the FIR (flight information region) service. Note that both the UIR and FIR are *advisory* services: they provide information for pilots but do not control the movement of aircraft.

A further advisory service is available for small aircraft on VFR flights: LARS (lower airspace radar service). The facility is provided by the various MATZ (military aerodrome traffic zones) up and down the country. Again, they do not control flights but merely offer information regarding other aircraft in the area.

Company frequencies
Most airlines use 'company frequencies'. Any one frequency, however, may be used by several airline operators to contact company ground stations. An example of the use of company frequencies could be when an aircraft wishes to contact the operations department of the company base at the destination airfield, in order to give the estimated time of arrival or request special services such as wheelchairs for invalid passengers. Other messages may concern servicing required on the aircraft: instruments may need adjusting, or there may be minor technical problems that engineers will need to correct before the aircraft takes-off again.

Glossary
The following list of abbreviations and expressions are regularly used during typical transmissions between ground and air.

Abort Abandon (ie, abandon take-off).

AFIS Airfield flight information service.

AIREP Report for position and weather in flight.

Airway Defined flight path.

amsl Above mean sea level.

APU Auxiliary power unit (backup when engines are off).

ASDA Runway accelerated stop distance.

ASI Air speed indicator.

ATA Actual time of arrival.

ATC Air traffic control.

ATIS Automatic terminal information service.

avgas Aviation grade petrol.

Avionics Aircraft electronics.

Backtrack Taxi back down the runway.

Beacon Station transmitting continuous navigation signal.

CAT Clear air turbulence.

CBs Cumulo nimbus (thunder clouds).

Conflicting Conflicting traffic, etc, possible collision course.

Decimal Decimal point as in frequency, eg, 128.65MHz.

Cav-OK Ceiling and visibility are good.

DF Direction finding by radio.

DME Distance measuring equipment.

Drift Lateral movement off desired track.

ETA Estimated time of arrival.

FIR Flight information region.

Flameout Total power loss on jet or turbo prop engine.

Gear Undercarriage.

Glidepath Line of descent on landing.

GMC Ground movement controller.

GMT Greenwich mean time.

Go around Overshoot runway and re-join circuit.

GPU Ground power unit.

Greens Landing gear down and locked indicators.

Homer Homing beacon.

IAS Indicated air speed.

IFR Instrument flight rules.

ILS Instrument landing system.

IMC Instrument meteorological conditions.

JET A1 Jet and turbo-prop fuel (kerosene).

Knots Nautical miles per hour.

LARS Lower airspace radar service.

Localiser Glidepath beacon.

Mach Speed in relation to the speed of sound.

MATZ Military aerodrome traffic zone.

METAR Meterological report (not a forecast).

Navaid Navigational aid.

NavCom Combined communication and navigation radio.

Navex Navigation exercise (training flight).

NDB Non-directional beacon.

NOTAM Notice to airmen.

Okta An eighth. Used to denote cloud density.

Ops Operations.

Orbit Fly in a circle.

Overshoot No longer used, see 'go around'.

Pax Passengers (eg, 64 pax on board).

PAR Precision approach radar.

PPO Prior permission only (restricted airfields).

QDM Magnetic heading.

QFE Barometric pressure at aerodrome.

QNH Barometric pressure at sea level.

Roll-out Stopping distance after touchdown.

RSR Route surveillance radar.

RVR Runway visual range.

SAR Search and rescue.

SELCAL Selective calling system (activates radio by code).

SID Standard instrument departure.

SIG Significant.

SitRep Situation report.

Squawk Switch transponder on.

Squawk ident Select 'identification' mode on transponder.

SRE Surveillance radar element.

STOL Short take-off and landing.

Stratus Low misty cloud (often obscures runway approach).

TAI True air speed indicator.

TACAN Tactical air navigator.

TAF Terminal area forecast.

TAR Terminal area radar.

TAS True air speed.

TMA Terminal control area.

Traffic Aircraft in flight.

UIR Upper flight information region.

US Unserviceable.

UTC Universal time constant (GMT).

VASI Runway lights angled to give a visual glide slope.

VFR Visual flight rules.

VMC Visual meteorological conditions.

VOLMET Continuous weather forecast.

VOR VHF omni-direction range beacon.

VSI Vertical speed indicator (rate of climb).

VTOL Vertical take-off and landing.

WX Weather.

NASA Shuttles

Three UHF frequencies (see Chapter 7) have been used by the NASA shuttles over the years but it should be noted that on some missions, the communications have been restricted to frequencies which are outside the range of ordinary scanners. However, UHF communications are heard on some flights, particularly those involving spacewalks (EVA — Extra Vehicular Activity).

It must be stressed that Shuttle communications are unlikely to be heard on a scanner which is simply being used with an ordinary discone antenna. A Helix antenna (proper helix — not the rubber duck type) or crossed dipoles designed for the frequency and a masthead pre-amplifier are advisable for best results.

The following abbreviations are ones commonly used during the lift-off phase (frequently re-broadcast via the media) and during some stages of the flight.

AFSCN Air Force Satellite Control Network.
ALT Approach for Landing Test programme.
AMU Astronaut manouvering unit.
APS Alternate Payload Specialist.
APU Auxiliary Power Unit.
ASE Airborne Support Equipment.
ATE Automatic Test Equipment.
ATO Abort to Orbit.
BFC Backup Flight Control.
CAPCOM Capsule Communicator.
CCAFS Cape Canaveral Air Force Station.
CCMS Checkout, Control and Monitor Sub-systems.
CDR Commander.
CDMS Command and Data Management Systems Officer.
CDS Central Data Systems.
CIC Crew Interface Coordinator.
CIE Communications Interface Equipment.
CTS Call to Stations.
DCC Data Computation Complex.
DCS Display Control System.
DIG Digital Image Generation.
DFI Development Flight Instrumentation.
DFRF Dryden Flight Research Facility.
DMC Data Management Coordinator.
DOD Department of Defence.
DPS Data Processing System.
EAFB Edwards Air Force Base.
ECLSS Environmental Control and Life Support System.

EMU Extra Vehicular Mobility Unit.
ESMC Eastern Space and Missile center.
ET External Tank.
EVA Extra Vehicular Activity.
FAO Flight Activities Officer.
F/C Flight Controller.
FD Flight Director.
FDO Flight Dynamics Officer.
FOD Flight Operations Directorate.
FOE Flight Operations Engineer.
FOSO Flight Operations Scheduling Officer.
FR Firing Room.
FRC Flight Control Room.
FRCS Forward Reaction Control System.
FRF Flight Readiness Firing.
FRR Flight Readiness Review.
GAS Getaway Special.
GC Ground Control.
GDO Guidance·Officer.
GLS Ground Launch Sequencer.
GN Ground Network.
GNC Guidance, Navigation and Control Systems Engineer.
GPC General Purpose Computer.
GSE Ground Support Equipment.
GSFC Goddard Space Flight center.
IG Inertial Guidance.
ILS Instrument Landing System.
IMF In-Flight Maintenance.
INCO Instrumentation and Communications Officer.
IUS Inertial Upper Stage.
IVA Intra Vehicular Activity.
JSC Johnson Space center.
KSC Kennedy Space center.
LC Launch Complex
LCC Launch Control center.
LCS Launch Control System.
LOX Liquid Oxygen.
LPS Launch Processing System.
MCC Mission Control center.
MD Mission Director.
ME Main Engine.
MECO Main Engine Cut-Off.
MET Mission Elapsed Time.
MLS Microwave Landing System.
MOD Mission Operations Directorate.

MOP Mission Operations Plan.
MPS Main Propulsion System.
MS Mission Specialist.
MSCI Mission Scientist.
MSFC Marshall Space Flight center.
NASCOM Nasa Communications Network.
NOCC Network Operations Control center.
NSRS NASA Safety Reporting System.
OAA Orbiter Access Arm.
OC Operations Coordinator.
OFI Operational Flight Instrumentation.
OMS Orbiter Manouvering System.
PDRS Payload Deployment and Retrieval System.
PLT Pilot
POD Payload Operations Director.
PS Payload Specialist.
RMS Remote Manipulator System.
RTLS Return to Launch Site.
SIP Standard Interface Panel.
SLF Shuttle Landing Facility.
SN Space Network.
SPOC Shuttle Portable On-board Computer.
SRB Solid Rocket Booster.
SRM Solid Rocket Motor.
SSC Stennis Space center.
SSCP Small Self-Contained Payload.
SSP Standard Switch Panel.
SSME Space Shuttle Main Engines.
TACAN Tactical Air Navigation.
TAL Trans-Atlantic Abort Landing.
TDRS Tracking Data and Relay Satellite.
WSMC Western Space and Missile center.

Scanner and accessories 9
review

A look at the equipment available in Britain

This chapter looks at the equipment which is on offer from British dealers and if you own the original *Scanners 1* book you will see that the range has increased and that Bearcat scanners are back on the market as well as some new names such as Black Jaguar, Cobra and Kenwood.

In order to keep the review to manageable proportions I have deleted some of the obsolete scanners which were included in the first edition because they were still widely available on the second-hand market. Instead, and in response to comments from readers, I have included some general notes on what to look for when buying used equipment.

In the case of new equipment the specifications quoted are those claimed by the manufacturer. The comments which accompany some models are my own and based either on personal experience with the scanner or general impressions gained from friends and trade sources. Although I have owned many scanners (and according to my wife still own far too many) the comments should not be interpreted as a recommendation for any particular model.

Buying guide

If you have read the book so far you should have a fairly good idea by now which features you want on a scanner and should be able to choose one from the information given in this chapter. However let us recap on a few points.

Scanner buyers broadly fall into one of three categories: those whose interest lies in just one band (usually airband or marine enthusiasts), those whose interest covers a limited range of two or more bands and finally those enthusiasts who want to be able to tune most, if not all, of the VHF/UHF range.

Airband scanners

Although the majority of scanners cover the airband, many of them offer performance which is something of a compromise. Airband transmissions are AM mode and the ideal circuitry for AM differs to that for FM. Although the majority of dual or multimode scanners offer adequate performance on airband, they rarely achieve the same level of performance as dedicated airband scanners such as the Sony, WIN or Signal models where the RF, IF and AGC circuits are optimised for the band and mode.

Banded scanners

These are scanners which offer coverage of selected bands in the VHF and UHF ranges. Their coverage is normally of those bands which are of most interest to scanner enthusiasts but you should be aware that some sets are aimed at the US market and others at the European market and both types are on sale in Britain. The difference between the two is usually in the lower frequency ranges and typically the US versions cover 29-54MHz whilst European versions cover 65-88MHz (PMR and emergency service 'LOW' bands) instead.

Typically, banded scanners will cover the above mentioned bands together with the 118-174MHz and 406-512MHz. These cover the majority of air, marine and land mobile bands but one point to watch is that most banded scanners do not allow you to switch between AM and FM. Instead, where airband is included, the scanner automatically switches to AM only when tuned to the airband. For some scanner buyers in Britain this can be a distinct disadvantage as AM is still quite widely used by some services in other bands. Two notable exceptions to this are the Revco RS3000 and the Black Jaguar, and some AOR and Regency handhelds where the mode is programmed into memory along with the frequency. The Black Jaguar is also unusual in that it offers coverage of the military airband between 200-280 and 360-520MHz.

Wideband scanners

These are the most versatile of scanners and AOR were the first to venture into the field with their classic AR2001 which covered 25-550MHz with no gaps and offered programmable selection of AM and narrow or wide FM on any frequency. Subsequently the AR2002, Regency and Realistic models have followed with tuning as high as 1300MHz and the only band omitted in some cases being 500-800MHz which is the television broadcast band. Yaesu (SSB as well as the usual AM/FM) and Kenwood have models that scan up to just over 900MHz and in the case of the Kenwood you even get Long, Medium and Short wave coverage as well. The ultimate machines in this class are the Icom R7000 and AOR AR3000 with multimode and coverage up to 2000MHz.

Where to buy

The most important advice is to buy from a dealer who will have proper facilities to repair any equipment he sells you. Statistically, if your new scanner is going to break down it will do so in the first few weeks you own it and there can be nothing more infuriating than waiting for weeks or even months for it to be repaired. If you buy a scanner from a dealer who specialises in this kind of equipment (most amateur radio equipment shops do have facilities) then repair should be fairly fast. On the other hand if you buy from the corner shop that sells a few TV's, radios and household appliances they are unlikely to have the kind of sophisticated equipment nor the experience to repair or re-align sophisticated VHF/UHF equipment. Never mind what the salesman says, it is a specialised area of servicing.

With a specialised dealer you will also get proper advice on choosing a scanner. Salesmen who work in the majority of amateur radio type shops are usually enthusiasts and know their products well. On the other hand I could fill a book with some of the fantastic claims and howlers I have heard pour from the mouths of shop assistants selling scanners in Hi-fi/TV shops.

Buying used equipment.

Used equipment is often advertised in the small advertisement sections of the many magazines devoted to amateur radio and hobbyist electronics. When buying a used scanner the first thing to check is the frequency coverage and, if it is important to your choice of listening, whether or not the mode is selectable on all bands. For instance, the Bearcat 220 and its many variants regularly appear these days and although they have fair performance they do not allow AM reception on any frequencies other than airband.

When checking a scanner prior to purchase take a careful look at its general appearance. In the days when I used to service such equipment it became obvious that the majority of scanners appearing on the service bench looked as if they had been ill-treated. Dented or cracked cases, holes drilled in the cases and loose or broken controls. Also watch out for case screws which have chewed-up heads — a sure sign that someone has been at the innards. Beware of any scanner that looks as if it has been modified or tinkered with. If you can arrange to try the scanner for a day or two (offer a deposit if you have to) and see if it is possible to have a look inside the casing (watch how you treat the case screws though). Check for any signs of repairs or modifications and pay particular attention to tuning coil slugs. Any wax seals over them should be completely untouched and closely inspect any exposed ones to make sure that there are no minute chips around the adjustment slots or that the slugs themselves are cracked. Note that alignment of some scanners can be a costly affair and unless you own some very sophisticated test equipment you will not be able to do it yourself.

I may seem a little cynical in my above comments but experience in the trade has shown that very many people just do not seem to be able to resist the temptation of having a 'tweak'. The worst offenders are often those people with a little knowledge of radio circuitry and so be doubly cautious if the seller seems to be well versed in technology.

Obviously you should ask for a demonstration of the scanner and do not be afraid to ask if the owner has had any problems with it or had it repaired.

Prices

I have avoided listing prices in this edition of 'Scanners' as currency fluctuations on world currency markets can lead to quite dramatic price swings. A glance at a current issue of a magazine aimed at the amateur radio or electronic hobbyist market will usually reveal dealer advertisements carrying up to date prices. The small ads' in the same magazines will usually give a good guide to second-hand prices as well.

Model: AOR AR2002.
Type: Base/mobile.

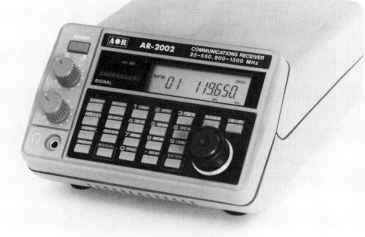

Receiver type: Triple conversion/up-conversion.
Coverage: 25-550, 800-1300MHz.
Quoted sensitivity: NFM 0.3uV (12dB SINAD)
　　　　　　　　　WFM 1.0uV (12dB SINAD)
　　　　　　　　　AM 0.5uV (10dB S/N)

Selectivity: NFM ±7.5KHz @ 6dB — ±20KHz @ 70dB.
  WFM ±50KHz @ 6dB — ±250KHz @ 60dB.
  Am ±5KHz @ 6dB — ±10KHz @ 70dB.
Modes and selection: WFM, NFM, AM. User selectable.
Search: User defined limits at 5/12.5/25KHz steps up or down.
Memory channels: 20.
Programming: Keypad with dual function keys and rotary tuning.
Priority: Fixed as channel one.
Delay: All channels or none.
Lockout: Any memory channels.
Display: LCD with backlight, Bargraph LED S-meter.
Power source: 12V DC (mains adaptor supplied).
External connections: Antenna (BNC), headphones, extension speaker, DC power, computer pack interface.
Additional features: Supplied with telescopic antenna and power lead for mobile use. Mobile mounting bracket and computer control pack (RC-Pack) available as extras.
Comments: A classic amongst scanners. It has excellent sensitivity across its entire frequency range and is very compact. The only drawbacks are limited number of memory channels and the rather slow scan rate (in *Scanners 2* a modification is described to speed it up). Its predecessor was the AR2001 which covered 25-550MHz but had no manual tuning knob nor S-meter but still with the same performance.

AOR AR2125

Readers of the American magazines which now filter into Britain will have noticed that the AR2125 is now on sale in the USA in place of the AR2002. It offers the same performance and is identical in appearance but several improvements have been made. First, the frequency coverage extends from 5.0MHz to 1500MHz and there are 2000 memory channels and 16 user defined search ranges available. The scanning rate has been speeded up considerably and RS-232 style computer interface has been built into the scanner.

However, this scanner will not become available in Britain because it is a specially modified version of the 2002. AOR scanners are sold exclusively by mail order in the USA by a firm called ACE who are the importers. In the case of the 2125, ACE remove the existing control circuit boards and replace them with their own design which provides the improved performance.

However, Lowe Electronics who are the British distributors say they have looked at the idea of importing these sets but by the time various costs such as freight and import duty are added the final cost is not far short of the price of the AR3000 which offers far better performance.

Model: AOR AR3000.

Type: Base/mobile.

Receiver type: Triple conversion superhetrodyne on all bands and modes except WBFM where quadruple conversion is used.

Coverage: 100KHz-2.036GHz (yes GigaHertz) via 13 bandpass filters into GaSFET amplifiers.

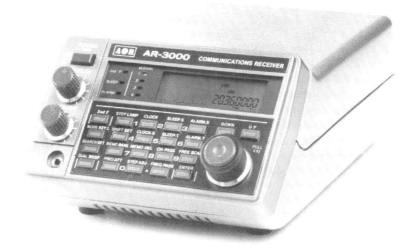

Quoted sensitivity: 1.000—2.500MHz = 1.0uV for SSB/CW or
        3.2uV for AM (10dB SINAD)
        2.5MHz—1.8GHz = 0.25uV for SSB/CW or
        1.0uV for AM (10dB SINAD)
        2.5MHz—1.8GHz = 0.35uV for NFM or
        1.0uV for WBFM (12dB SINAD)
        1.8GHz—2.0GHz = 0.75uV for SSB/CW or
        1.0uV for AM (10dB SINAD)
        1.8GHz—2.0GHz = 1.25uV for NFM or
        3.0uV for WBFM (12dB SINAD)

Selectivity: 2.4KHz—6dB, 4.5KHz—60dB (USB/LSB/CW)
      12KHz—6dB, 25KHz—70dB (AM/NFM)
      180KHz—6dB, 800KHz—50dB (WBFM)

Modes: WFM, NFM, AM, USB, LSB, CW.

Search: User defined limits (4 search banks or more).

Memory channels: 400 (4 x 100) scanned at 20 per second, recording frequency, mode, step and attenuator setting.

Programming: Keypad.

Priority: 1 channel per memory bank.

Delay: Programmable.

Lockout: Programmable.

Display: LCD with backlight showing Frequency, step rates, channel number, S-meter, mode, etc.

Power source: 12VDC (mains adaptor supplied).

External connections: Computer control port, automatically selected antenna sockets (BNC for HF and VHF/UHF), 12VDC, extension loudspeaker and auxiliary port (no details given in provisional specifications).

Additional features: Rotary tuning control, alarm/timer and extensive control over operation.

Comments: Not available at the time of writing but if the specifications are true then grovel in front of your bank manager.

Model: AOR AR800E.

Type: Handheld portable.

Receiver type: Not stated.

Coverage: 70—105, 118—174, 406—495, 803—950MHz.

Quoted sensitivity: VHF/NFM @ 0.5uV, UHF/NFM @ 0.7uV,
             AM @ 1.0uV

Selectivity: Not stated.

Modes: AM/FM programmable on any range.

Search: 5, 10, 12.5, 25KHz steps within user defined limits

Memory channels: 20.

Programming: Keypad.

Priority: No.

Delay: Yes.

Lockout: Yes.

Display: LCD.

Power source: Internal 4.8V NiCad pack (supplied).

External connections: Charger, earphone & antenna (BNC).

Additional features: Supplied with NiCads and charger (doubles as a mains PSU).

Comments: Exceptionally compact and programmable AM/FM but I have tested several of these scanners at random and found sensitivity to be slightly below the figures claimed by the manufacturer on the VHF high ranges and some owners report a very large number of spurious signals (birdies) around 80MHz. Despite that, the small size and facilities have made it very popular.

Model: AOR AR900.

Type: Handheld portable.

Receiver type: Double conversion superhetrodyne.

Coverage: 108—174, 220—380, 406—470, 830—950MHz.

Quoted sensitivity: 0.4uV for VHF/NFM, 0.8uV for AM airband,
                0.5uV for UHF, 1.0uV for 800MHz band.

Selectivity: Not stated.

Modes: AM/FM programmable on any range.

Search: User defined limits on 5 pre-set search bands.

Memory channels: 100 (5 banks of 20) scanned at 15 channels per second.

Programming: Keypad.

Priority: Fixed channel.

Delay: Programmable on individual channels.

Lockout: Individual channels or by memory bank.

Display: LCD showing frequency, step, mode, etc.

Power source: Internal NiCad pack (supplied).

External connections: Earphone, charge socket and antenna (BNC).

Additional features: NiCad charger supplied.

Comments: Plenty of memory and AM/FM on any frequency. Includes coverage of the military UHF band but there is no coverage of the Low Band PMR or emergency frequencies.

Model: Bearcat 100XL.

Type: Handheld portable.
Receiver type: Double conversion superhetrodyne.
Coverage: 66—88MHz, 118—174MHz, 406—512MHz.
Quoted sensitivity: 66—88 & 136—174MHz = 0.4uV, 118—136MHz = 0.8uV, UHF = 0.5uV (all for 12dB SINAD)
Selectivity: 50dB @ ±25KHz
Modes: FM/AM (airband only).
Search: User defined limits.
Memory channels: 16 scanned at 15 per second.
Programming: Keypad.
Priority: Fixed on channel 1 (scanned every 2 seconds).
Delay: 3 second on any defined channel.
Lockout: Any channel.
Display: LCD (backlight with auto-shutdown).
Power source: 12V DC (external) or 7.2V DC internal NiCads (supplied).
External connections: 12V DC, earphone, antenna (BNC).
Additional features: Supplied with carry case, NiCads, charger and antenna.
Comments: Solid, well-made, middle of the road portable with all the accessories supplied as standard. Some users may find 16 memory channels a bit low.

Model: Bearcat 175XL.

Type: Base.
Receiver type: Not stated.
Coverage: 66—88MHz, 118—174MHz, 406—512MHz.

Quoted sensitivity: 66—88MHz, 136—174MHz = 0.3uV,
                   118—136MHz = 0.8uV, UHF = 0.5uV
                   (all for 12dB SINAD).
Selectivity: -45dB ±25KHz
Modes: FM/AM (airband only).
Search: User defined limits.
Memory channels: 16 scanned at 5 or 15 seconds per channel.
Programming: Keypad.
Priority: Channel 1 (checked every 2 seconds).
Delay: Programmable onto any channel.
Lockout: Any channel.
Display: LCD with backlight.
Power source: 240VAC.
External connections: Loudspeaker, power, antenna
Additional features: Supplied with telescopic antenna

Model: Bearcat 100XLT and Bearcat 200XLT.

Type: Handheld portable.

Receiver type: Not stated.

Coverage: 66—88MHz, 118—174MHz, 406—512MHz, 806—956MHz (200XLT)

Quoted sensitivity: 66—88MHz & 136—174MHz = 0.4uV,
        118—136MHz = 0.8uV, 406—512MHz = 0.5uV
        (all for 12dB SINAD). 806—956MHz not quoted.

Sensitivity: 50dB ±25KHz.

Modes: FM/AM (airband only).

Search: User defined limits.

Memory channels: 100XLT = 100 (5 x 20), 200XLT = 200 (10 x 20) scanned at 15 channels per second.

Programming: Keypad.

Priority: Yes.

Delay: Programmable.

Lockout: Programmable onto any channel.

Display: LCD with backlight.

Power source: 12V DC (external) or 7:2V DC from detachable cell pack.

External connections: 12V DC, earphone, antenna (BNC).

Dimensions: 7.5″ x 2.8″ x 1.4″ (1lb 4oz).

Additional features: Supplied with NiCad pack and charger, carry case and antenna.

Comments: These portables are Bearcat's top of the range models and the 200XLT is typical of the new thinking on portables where the 806—956MHz band is being included. Both are well made and the detachable battery pack is a useful feature if spare packs are to be carried to cover prolonged use.

Model: Bearcat 210XW (not shown).

Type: Base/mobile.

Receiver type: Double conversion superhetrodyne.

Coverage: 29—50MHz, 136—174MHz, 406—512MHz

Quoted sensitivity: Not stated.

Selectivity: Not stated.

Modes: FM only.

Search: User defined limits.

Memory channels: 20.

Programming: Keypad.

Priority: Channel 1 (checked every 2 seconds).

Delay: Programmable onto any channel.

Lockout: Any channel.

Display: Led.

Power source: 240V AC or 12V DC.

External connections: Loudspeaker, power, antenna (motorola plug).

Additional features: Supplied with telescopic antenna.

Comments: No Low or Airband coverage (you can actually get 4MHz more coverage by buying the same firm's 50XL portable at getting on for half the price). The casing is virtually identical to the long obsolete 220 range and I am puzzled by Uniden's release of this scanner which seems to be about the worst value for money I have ever encountered and yet on a recent visit to the USA, there seemed to be one sat in just about every electronics shop.

Model: Bearcat 50XL and 55XLT.

Type: Portable.

Receiver type: Double conversion superhetrodyne.

Coverage: 29—54 (55XLT) or 66—88MHz (50XL), 136—174MHz, 406—512MHz.

Quoted sensitivity: Low band = 0.4uV, mid & UHF band = 0.7uV
                              (all for 12dB SINAD).

Selectivity: -55dB ±25KHz.

Modes: FM only.

Search: No.

Memory channels: 10 scanned at 10 per second.
Programming: Keypad.
Priority: No.
Delay: 3 second (cannot be switched off).
Lockout: Any channels.
Display: 2-digit LCD.
Power source: 7.5V DC internal penlight cells or external 12V DC.
External connections: 12V DC, earphone, antenna (BNC).
Dimensions: 68mm x 35mm x 170mm (300g).
Additional features: Supplied with belt clip and helical antenna.
Comments: This is a well made, no-frills, budget price scanner. Nice touches include an internal switch to select dry cell or NiCad use with the latter being recharged at the correct rate by simply plugging in a 12V DC supply. Buyers should check that they get a sample which has the Low Band coverage they want (US or UK).

Model: Bearcat 580XL and 950XLT.

Type: Base/mobile.
Receiver type: Not stated.
Coverage: 29—54MHz, 118—174MHz, 410—512MHz, 806—956MHz (950XLT).
Quoted sensitivity: 29—54 & 136—174MHz = 0.4uV (12dB SINAD)
                      118—136MHz = 0.8uV (for 60% modulation)
                      406—512MHz = 0.4uV (12dB SINAD)
Selectivity: -55dB @ ±25KHz
Modes: FM and AM (airband only).
Search: User defined or pre-set on air and marine bands.
Memory channels: 100 channels (5 banks of 20) scanned at 15 per second.
Programming: Keypad.
Priority: Fixed on channel 1 (sampled every 2 seconds).
Delay: User defined or all channels with 3 second delay.
Lockout: Yes.

Display: LCD (backlit).
Power sources: 12V DC (mains adaptor available).
External connections: Antenna, loudspeaker, 12V DC.
Dimensions: 161mm x 42mm x 188mm (1.05kg).
Additional features: Mobile bracket available as an extra.
Comments: Very smart and compact mobile unit with very fast scan rate. However, prospective buyers should note that UK Low Band is not available and AM/FM selection is automatic according to band. Both models are identical except the 950XLT covers the 806—956MHz band.

Model: Bearcat 70XLT (not shown).
Type: Pocket portable.
Receiver type: Double conversion superhetrodyne.
Coverage: 66—88MHz, 136—174MHz, 406—512MHz.
Quoted sensitivity: Low band = 0.4uV, mid band = 0.5uV, UHF band
$\qquad\qquad$ = 0.7uV (all for 12dB SINAD).
Selectivity: -55dB ±25KHz.
Modes: FM only.
Search: User defined limits.
Memory channels: 20 scanned at 15 per second.
Programming: Keypad.
Priority: Channel 1, scanned every 2 seconds.
Delay: 2 seconds (cannot be switched off).
Lockout: Any channels.
Display: LCD with backlight.
Power source: 4.8V DC internal NiCad cells or external 12V DC.
External connections: 12V DC, earphone, antenna (BNC).
Dimensions: 70mm x 156mm x 26mm (300g).
Additional features: Supplied with NiCad charger, case and helical antenna.
Comments: Possibly the first true pocket portable. This little scanner packs a lot of features for its size but it does lack Airband coverage.

Model: Bearcat 800XLT (not shown).
Type: Base/mobile.
Receiver type: Not stated.
Coverage: 29—54MHz, 118—174MHz, 406—512MHz, 840—912MHz.
Quoted sensitivity: 29—54MHz, 136—174MHz = 0.6uV,
$\qquad\qquad$ 118—136MHz = 0.8uV, UHF = 0.8uV,
$\qquad\qquad$ 840—912MHz = 1.0uV (all for 12dB SINAD).
Selectivity: -55dB ±25KHz.
Modes: FM/AM (airband only).
Search: User defined limits.
Memory channels: 40.
Programming: Keypad.
Priority: Channel 1 (checked every 2 seconds).

Delay: Programmable onto any channel.
Lockout: Any channel.
Display: Led.
Power source: 240V AC or 12V DC.
External connections: Loudspeaker, power, antenna.
Additional features: Supplied with telescopic antenna.
Comments: No UK Low Band coverage and I am not sure the 806—912MHz band is of particular interest to British users. The scanner is quite bulky (similar to the old 220 models).

Model: Black Jaguar BJ200 mkIII.
Type: Portable.
Receiver type: Not stated.

Coverage: 26—30MHz, 50—88MHz, 115—178MHz, 200—280MHz, 360—520MHz.
Quoted Sensitivity: FM: 0.5uV for HF and VHF, 0.7uV for UHF (all 12dB SINAD). AM: 1.0uV for HF and VHF, 1.5uV for UHF (all 10dB SINAD).
Selectivity: 60dB ±20KHz.

Modes: AM/FM programmable on any channel.
Search: User defined limits.
Memory channels: 16 scanned at 10 per second.
Programming: Keypad.
Priority: Yes.
Delay: 2 seconds.
Lockout: Yes.
Display: LCD.
Power source: Internal 600mAH sealed NiCad pack (charger supplied).
External connections: Charge, earphone, antenna (N-type).
Additional features: Supplied with NiCads/charger, carry case, etc. Fast/slow chargers, vehicle power supply adaptors, UHF helical antenna, UHF vehicle magmount and car mount and desk brackets are available as extras.
Comments: Very wide band coverage and programmable AM/FM have made this a popular scanner. Rather bulky and heavy but owners swear by the set's performance and coverage of some of the military UHF airband is unusual. The earlier mkII version is also available under the Challenger name but it should be noted that some Challenger models may not cover the UK Low Band allocation.

Model: Cobra SR925 (not shown but similar to Bearcat 175XL).
Type: Base/mobile.
Receiver type: Not stated.
Coverage: 29—54MHz, 118—174MHz, 406—512MHz.
Quoted sensitivity: 29—54MHz, 136—174MHz = 0.3uV,
                        118—136MHz = 0.7uV, UHF = 0.5uV
                        (all for 12dB SINAD).
Selectivity: -55dB ±25KHz.
Modes: FM/AM (airband only).
Search: User defined limits.
Memory channels: 16 scanned at 5 or 15 seconds per channel.
Programming: Keypad.
Priority: Channel 1 (checked every 2 seconds).
Delay: Programmable onto any channel.
Lockout: Any channel.
Display: LCD with backlight.
Power source: 12V DC or 240V AC via external adaptor.
External connections: Loudspeaker, power, antenna.
Additional features: Supplied with telescopic antenna.
Comments: Excellent value for money although some users may find the lack of UK Low Band a disadvantage.

Model: ICOM 1C-R7000.
Importer/Agent: ICOM UK.
Type: Base/mobile.
Receiver: Quadruple/triple/double conversion.
Coverage: 25—100MHz & 1025—2000MHz no gaps. Specifications are only guaranteed for the 25—1000MHz range.

Quoted sensitivity: FMN less 0.5uV (12dB SINAD)
                      FMW 20dB NQL —0dBu.
                      AM 10dB S/N —0dBu (1uV) or less.
                      SSB 10dB S/N —10dBu (0.3uV) or less.
Selectivity: FMN 15KHz @ 6dB or 9KHz @ 6dB.
              AM 9KHz @ 6dB.
              FMW 150KHz @ 6dB.
              SSB 2.8KHz @ 6dB.
Programming: Keypad.
Modes: FM narrow and wide, narrow AM and SSB.
Number of channels: 99.
Display: Dual colour fluorescent. Frequency, Mode, etc.
Search: Yes and with autowrite (automatic entry of frequency into memory). 100Hz + 1/5/10/12.5/25KHz.
Priority: Yes. Programmable.
Delay: No.
Lockout: Yes (selectable scan channels).
Power source: 12V DC or 240V AC.
Audio out: 2.5 Watts.

External connections: Full details not specified.
Manual tuning knob: Yes with lock on/off.
Dimensions: 303x127x319 (with projections).
Additional features: Noise blanker, S-Meter, various types of scan (full, programmed, by mode, priority, auto-write, etc). Optional extras include infra-red remote controller, voice synthesised frequency readout, mobile mounting bracket, computer interface and TV demodulator.
Comments: It has a massive range of features and very wide coverage. The price is high but this includes most of the circuitry required for external computer control.

A.R.E. Version

A.R.E. Communications (see dealer list) offer a modified version of the R7000 designated the IC-R7000HF which offers further coverage in the range 500KHz—30MHz and an additional 99 memories. A.R.E. will also adapt any existing R7000 receivers to include these features.

Model: ICOM IC-R9000 (not shown).
Type: Base.
Receiver type: Multi conversion superhetrodyne.
Coverage: 100KHz—1999.8MHz.
Quoted sensitivity:

Range	SSB	AM	FM	WFM
0.1—0.5MHz	.5uV	1.0uV		
0.5—1.8MHz	1.0uV	6.3uV		
1.8—30MHz	0.16uV	0.5uV	0.5uV	
30—1000MHz	0.32uV	1.0uV	0.5uV	1.0uV
1000—1240MHz	0.63uV	4.0uV	1.0uV	4.0uV
1240—1300MHz	0.32uV	2.0uV	0.5uV	2.0uV
1300—1600MHz	0.63uV	4.0uV	1.0uV	4.0uV
1600—1999MHz	1.0uV	5.6uV	1.4uV	5.6uV

(10dB S/N for SSB, CW, FSK and AM — 12dB SINAD for FM and WFM).

Selectivity: SSB/CW/FSK more than 2.4KHz/-6dB
    AM more than 6KHz/-6dB
    FM more than 15KHz/-6dB
    WFM more than 150KHz/-6dB
Modes: FM, WBFM, AM (narrow and wide) & SSB (upper and lower sidebands are switch selectable), CW and FSK (Frequency shift keying)
Search: Between any user defined limits with autowrite to memory on up to 100 channels.
Memory channels: 1000 (10 x 100).

Programming: Keypad or rotary tuning knob with stepping rates of 10 & 100Hz, 1, 5, 9, 10, 12.5, 25 or 100KHz increments.

Priority: Programmable on any channels.

Delay: Yes. Variable speed.

Lockout: Yes. Individual channels or lock by mode or selection of blocks of memory channels.

Display: 5 inch CRT (cathode ray tube) type monitor which displays all scanning and frequency data, lists timers, etc and includes a spectrum analyser with ±100KHz bandwidth. The monitor screen can also be fed from an external video input.

Power source: 230V AC.

External connections: 3 antenna sockets for HF, VHF/UHF and UHF high, 10.7MHz IF output, scan operated tape recorder switch, headphones, external loudspeaker, serial data jack for computer control, video & spare phono socket for customised connections.

Additional features: Noise blanker (width and threshold adjustable), IF shift and notch controls. S-Meter (can be switched for center-zero tuning) various types of scan (full memory range, by mode only, priority, etc). There are several squelch modes and it will even switch a tape recorder on and off when signals are received. 2 timers are included for alarm and switching purposes.

Comments: The scanner owes its origins to the R7000 which broke new ground by taking scanning out of the realm of 'technotoys' and into the professional/commercial market. At the time of writing the R9000, which obviously tries to go several steps further, was not actually available but some comments had been made by colleagues on the published specifications. Bearing in mind the far higher cost compared with the R7000, specifications such as sensitivity do not appear to have been improved. There appears to be no way of individually locking out the memory channels and the so called spectrum analyser would be of limited use because of the small bandwidth available.

Model: JIL SX-200.

Importer/Agent: Garex.

Type: Synthesised base/mobile.

Receiver: Double conversion (10.7MHz/455KHz).

Coverage: 26—88, 108—180, 380—514MHz.

Quoted sensitivity: FM VHF 0.4uV (12dB S/N)
FM UHF 1.0uV (12dB S/N)
AM VHF 1.0uV (12dB S/N)
AM UHF 2.0uV (12dB S/N)

Selectivity: ±25KHz @ 60dB.

Programming: Keypad.

Modes: Narrow AM or FM (not programmable onto individual channels).

Number of channels: 16.
Display: Fluorescent.
Search: Yes. User defined limits. Step rate automatically selected; 5KHz below 58MHz and 12.5KHz above 58MHz.
Priority: No.
Delay: Yes. Not programmable (all or nothing).

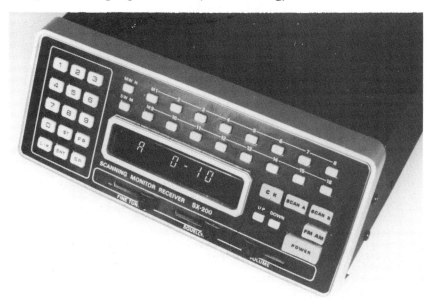

Lockout: Yes. Using Scan A or Scan B. Lockout channels are located in Scan B.
Power source: 12V or mains adaptor (supplied). 2 penlight cells for memory backup.
Audio out: 2 Watts.
External connections: 12V power. Recorder audio, external speaker, Tape recorder switch (needs external circuit). Antenna (Motorola).
Manual tuning knob: Yes. Fine tune only.
Dimensions: 8″ x 8″ x 2¾″ approx.
Additional features: Voice-squelch. Display dimmer.
Comments: When it first appeared it offered far more than its competitors but is now starting to show its age. The major drawback with the set is the inability to mix AM and FM. A very robust set, it has a solid metal case which acts as an effective screen against interference. Now rather expensive compared with other sets which offer far greater frequency range, facilities and sensitivity. Widely available on the second-hand market. *Scanners 2* includes some add-ons and modifications for this set including a front panel bargraph S-Meter and simultaneous AM/FM circuit.

Model: JIL SX-400.
Importer/Agents: Garex.
Type: Base/Mobile.
Receiver: Double conversion superhet.
Coverage: 26—520MHz (no gaps).
Quoted sensitivity: VHF FM (S/N = 312dB) 0.5uV
　　　　　　　　　　　　AM (S/N — 10dB) 1.0uV
　　　　　　　　　　UHF FM (S/N = 12dB) 0.5uV
　　　　　　　　　　　　AM (S/N = 10dB) 2.0uV

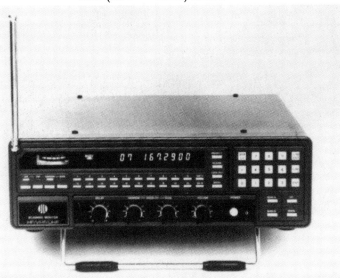

Signal/noise ratio: 45dB.
Selectivity: FM = 60dB at ±15KHz
　　　　　　　AM = 60dB at ±10KHz
　　　　　　　VHF image rejections = 50dB
Programming: Keypad.
Modes: AM/FM.
Number of channels: 20.
Display: Fluorescent.
Search: Yes. User defined limits.
Priority: Yes (pre-set channel).
Delay: Yes. 0—4 seconds variable.
Lockout: Yes and scanning can be across some or all 20 channels by allocating channels to either the 'B' block or 'A' (all channels) block.
Power source: 12V DC or 240V AC via optional adaptor.
Audio out: 4 Watt.
External connections: Antenna, 10.7MHz IF, External speaker, record audio, computer interface (IEEE(RS423 or RS232), external switching (tape recorder, etc), power in, converter/aerial switch socket for optional units.

Manual tuning knob: No.

Dimensions: 300x90x210mm.

Additional features: Signal strength meter, computer control, squelch 'width' selector, AM noise blanker, aerial attenuator and coverage possible from LF to 1.4GHz with optional converters.

Comments: This is a superbly built scanner but is, I feel, only likely to appeal to professional or commercial users. Surprisingly the AC adaptor is an extra.

Model: Kenwood RZ-1.

Type: Mobile (intended as a wideband car radio).

Receiver type: Triple superhetrodyne.

Coverage: 500KHz—905MHz.

Quoted sensitivity: AM (S + S/N = 10dB) less than 0.5uV (10uV on MW).
NFM (12dB SINAD) less than 6uV (500KHz—60MHz)
less than 3uV (60—905MHz)
WBFM (12dB SINAD) less than 1uV

Selectivity: AM 7KHz @ -6dB & 18KHz @ -50dB
FM 10KHz @ -6dB & 30KHz @ -50dB
WBFM 250KHz @ -6dB & 600KHz @ -30dB

Modes: WBFM, FM & AM auto-select or user defined.

Search: Yes between user defined limits.

Memory channels: 100 divided into 10 banks of 10.

Programming: Keypad or rotary tuning knob.

Priority: No.

Delay: Yes. Up to six seconds.

Lockout: Yes.

Display: LCD with user entry message of letters or numbers on each memory channel.

Power source: 12V DC

External connections: 12V DC, loudspeaker & antennae (automatically selected Motorola socket for MW and FM Broadcastbands and SO239 for other bands) and stereo line-level outputs.

Additional features: Loudspeakers and headphones available as extras, several squelch modes (NFM only).

Comments: Very wide coverage from LW upwards but the lack of SSB will limit usefulness on the HF bands. A major complaint from owners is that you cannot squelch in AM mode and even the importers admit they are not quite sure what to make of the RZ-1. Perhaps this is the ultimate car radio (which is what Kenwood intend it to be) for the owner of a Ferrari, Porsche or similar machine who likes something to fiddle with whilst parked on the M25.

Model: Lowe FS 10.

Importer/Agent: Lowe.
Type: Pocket portable.
Receiver: Double conversion (10.7MHz/455KHz).
Coverage: 70—80MHz or 130—170MHz (range must be stated when purchasing).
Quoted sensitivity: 0.3uV (12dB SINAD).
Selectivity: 12KHz BW @ 6dB.
Programming: Crystal.
Modes: FM only.
Number of channels: 10.
Display: LED lamp.
Search: No.
Priority: No.
Delay: No.

Lockout: No.

Power source: 5V DC from internal NiCad (supplied).

Audio out: 100mW approx.

External connections: External speaker, antenna (miniature jack) and rec.arge.

Manual tuning knob: No.

Dimensions: 127x71x35mm.

Additional features: Manual channel stepping allows selection of any one channel. Leatherette case available as optional extra. (Also sold under 'NIRECOM' label).

Comments: Very compact pocket portable. Limited bandwidth coverage limits 70—80MHz bandwidth and 130—170MHz version to 4MHz bandwidth. This means for instance that both the 2M amateur band and Marine Band could not be covered on the same set. The set is physically identical to the Lowe AP-12.

Model: LOWE AP-12 (Physically identical to Lowe FS-10)

Importer/Agent: Lowe.

Type: Pocket portable.

Receiver: Double conversion (10.7MHz/455KHz).

Coverage: 108—136MHz.

Quoted sensitivity: 0.5uV (10dB S/N).

Selectivity: 5.5KHz BW @ -6dB, 20KHz @ -40dB.

Programming: Crystal.

Modes: AM.

Number of channels: 12.

Display: LED lamp.

Search: No.

Priority: No.

Delay: Fixed.

Lockout: No.

Power source: 4.8V DC from internal NiCads (supplied).

Audio out: 100mW.

External connections: External speaker, external antenna (miniature jack) and re-charge.

Manual tuning knob: No.

Dimensions: 125x71x35mm.

Additional features: Manual step scanning for holding on any channel. Built in telescopic antenna.

Comments: Extremely compact for a 12 channel crystal controlled scanner. Dedicated set for airband only.

Model: Realistic Pro-34.

Type: Handheld portable.

Receiver type: Dual conversion superhetrodyne.

Coverage: 66—88, 108—174 (5KHz steps), 380—512, 806—960MHz (12.5KHz steps).

Quoted sensitivity: 66—88, 136—174, 380—520MHz =
1.0uV for 20dB S/N
108—136, 806—960 = 2.0uV for 20dB S/N

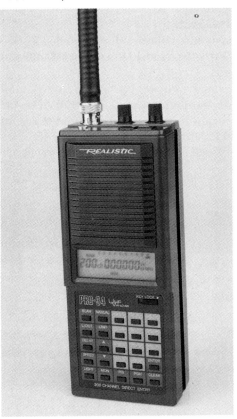

Selectivity: ±10KHz @ -6dB, ±20KHz @ -50dB

Modes: NFM and AM (airband only)

Search: User programmable at up to 16 steps per second.

Memory channels: 200 (10 banks of 20) and 10 temporary storage channels.

Programming: Keypad.

Priority: Programmed onto any one channel.

Delay: 2 seconds programmed onto any channels.

Lockout: Individual channels or banks can be locked-out.

Display: LCD showing frequency, channel, active memory banks, status (delay, priority, search, etc) and battery state.

Power source: 9V DC from 6X AA cells, NiCads or mains/vehicle adaptor

External connections: Charge, power, earphone, antenna (BNC).

Additional features: Helical antenna, internal charging regulator & battery saver circuit.

Comments: Tandy have always been very strong on their hand-held scanners and the Pro-34 is their best yet. The bands covered will satisfy very many users, the product is robust and well engineered. Bulky chargers are avoided with the built-in charge regulator which can be used whilst the set is being operated and the battery saver feature is something normally only found on professional equipment. In the saver mode, the scanner effectively switches off and on and only stays on when a signal is present. This means power savings of up to 60 percent can be made.

One final innovation is the inclusion of a 10 channel scratchpad memory where new frequencies can be temporarily stored. If you wish to keep them then they can be transferred to one of the 200 standard memory channels.

Model: Realistic PRO-38.

Type: Portable.
Receiver type: Double-conversion superhetrodyne.
Coverage: 66—88MHz, 136—174MHz, 406—512MHz.

Quoted sensitivity: Low band = 0.4uV, mid & UHF band = 0.7uV
(all for 12dB SINAD).

Selectivity: -55dB ±25KHz.

Modes: FM only.

Search: No.

Memory channels: 10 scanned at 10 per second.

Programming: Keypad.

Priority: No.

Delay: 3 second (cannot be switched off).

Lockout: Any channels.

Display: 2-digit LCD.

Power source: 7.5V DC internal penlight cells or external 12V DC.

External connections: 12V DC, earphone, antenna (BNC).

Dimensions: 68mm x 35mm x 170mm (300g).

Additional features: Supplied with belt clip and helical antenna.

Comments: Excellent value for money and could work out cheaper than some crystal controlled scanners (if you include the cost of crystals). No airband coverage but well-made and nice touches include an internal switch to select dry cell or NiCad use with the latter being recharged at the correct rate by simply plugging-in a 12v DC supply.

Model: Realistic Pro-57.

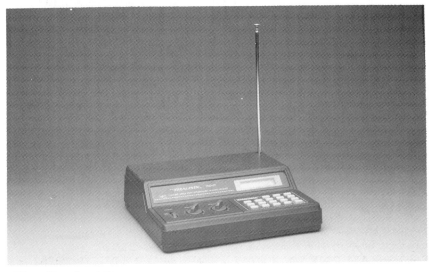

Type: Base/mobile.

Receiver type: Dual conversion superhetrodyne.

Coverage: 68—88, 138—174MHz (5KHz steps), 380—512MHz (12.5KHz steps)

Quoted sensitivity: All bands 1.0uV @ 20dB S/N with 3KHz deviation

Selectivity: ±10KHz @ -6dB and ±20KHz @ -5dB

Modes: FM only.
Search: No.
Memory channels: 10.
Programming: Keypad.
Priority: No.
Delay: 2 seconds on all channels or none.
Lockout: Any channel.
Display: LCD.
Power source: 12V DC or external mains adaptor.
External connections: 12V DC, antenna (Motorola socket).
Comments: An inexpensive, no-frills scanner ideal for use in the car or boat. Despite a lack of airband coverage and only 10 memory channels it represents good value for money.

Model: Realistic PRO-2021.

Type: Synthesised Base/mobile.
Receiver: Double conversion superhetrodyne (10.7/455 IF's)
Coverage: 66—88, 108—136, 138—174 and 380—512MHz.
Sensitivity: AM: 20dB S/N @ 60% modulation = 2.0uV. FM: 20dB
                    S/N @ 3KHz deviation; 66—88MHz = 0.5uV,
                    138—174MHz = 1.0uV, 380—512MHz = 1.0uV.
Selectivity: ±9KHz, -6dB/ ±15KHz, -50dB.
Programming: Keypad.
Modes: Automatic selection of AM or NBFM.
Number of channels: 200 in 10 banks of 20 and 10 monitor channels.

Scan/search rate: 8 or 4 steps per second.

Display: Liquid Crystal Display (LCD) showing frequency, mode, channel etc.

Priority: Yes. Sampled every 2 seconds.

Delay: 2 seconds.

Lockout: Yes.

Power source: 240V AC internal power supply of external 13.8V DC.

Audio out: 1 Watt into 8 Ohms.

External connections: Antenna (plug not stated), DC supply, tape outlet (phono) and External speaker.

Dimensions: 80Hx260Wx200D (mm) —2.0kg.

Comments: Supplied with telescopic and mobile mounting bracket. Automatic AM/FM selection could be a hindrance for some users but otherwise a good budget price scanner that will satisfy the needs of the user who solely wants to monitor say airband, marine and a few PMR or emergency channels.

Model: Realistic PRO-2004.

Type: Base/mobile.

Receiver: Type not stated but apparently triple-superhetrodyne.

Coverage: 25—520 and 760—1300MHz.

Quoted sensitivity: WBFM (30dB S/N @ 22.5KHz Dev.)
          25—1100MHz: 3uV 1.8uV
          1100—1300MHz: 10uV
          NBFM (20dB S/N @ 3KHz Dev.)
          25—520MHz 0.5uV 0.5uV
          760—1100MHz 0.3uV 0.5uV
          1100—1300MHz 3.0uV
          AM (20dB S/N @ 60% modulation)
          25—520MHz 2uV 1.7uV
          760—1100MHz 2.0uV 2.1uV
          1100—1300MHz 3.0uV

Selectivity: NFM and AM: ±9KHz @ -6dB. WFM: ±150KHz @ -6dB.

Programming: Membrane style keyboard.

Modes: Narrow AM and FM, wide FM. Mode is automatically selected according to band but can be overridden by keyboard command.

Number of channels: 300 memory channels divided into 10 banks of 30. Another 10 channels act as a 'scratch pad' to store frequencies found during searching.

Display: Liquid Crystal Display (LCD).

Search: Either in pre-determined blocks or user programmed.

Priority: User selected channel sampled every 2 seconds.

Delay: Yes. Programmable.

Scan/search rate: 16 or 8 steps/channels per second.

Lockout: Programmable on any channel.
Audio out: 1.8 Watts into 8 Ohms.
Power source: Internal AC power or external 13.8V DC.

External connections: Antenna (BNC), tape recorder (phono), external speaker, DC power.
Dimensions: 275W x 230D x 75H (mm).
Comments: Excellent value for money and at the price offers more features than some more expensive scanners. Despite the cheap 'n' cheerful membrane keyboard the 2004 is very easy and fast to drive. For many months during 1987 the 2004 was not available simply because world-wide demand outstripped supply. Nothing but praise from owners.

Model: Regency MX8000.
Comments: Identical to the AOR 2002.
Note: All Regency models are intended for the US market (110V AC mains) and so are not supplied with a mains converter in the UK. These are available as an optional extra.

Model: Revco RS3000.
Type: Base/mobile.
Receiver type: Double conversion superhetrodyne.
Coverage: 26—32MHz, 60—90MHz, 118—180MHz, 380—512MHz
Quoted sensitivity: FM: HF and VHF = 0.5uV, UHF = 0.8uV
(all 12 dB SINAD)

Selectivity: Not stated.
Modes: AM/FM programmable.
Search: User defined limits.
Memory channels: 50.
Programming: Keypad.
Priority: Channel 1.
Delay: Yes.
Lockout: Individually or in banks of 10 memory channels.
Display: LCD.
Power source: 12v DC (mains adaptor not supplied).
External connections: Loudspeaker, power, antenna (Motorola).
Additional features: Supplied with mobile mounting kit.
Comments: Budget priced scanner featuring the all important (for British users) programmable AM and FM. It will satisfy the needs of many users and although sensitivity is quite good the set is rather prone to image and blocking problems if you live close to the source of any strong local transmissions.

Model: Revco RS4000 (not shown).
Type: Base/mobile.
Coverage: 26—950MHz.
Modes: AM/FM programmable.
Search: User defined limits.
Memory channels: 100.
Programming: Keypad.
Comments: At the time of going to print the new RS4000 was not actually available. However, it is known that it will be a budget priced receiver clearly aimed at the market once held by the AOR AR2001 and now dominated by the Realistic PRO-2004.

Model: Signal R528.
Importer/Agent: Lowe.

Type: Crystal control portable.
Coverage: 118—136MHz (airband).
Quoted sensitivity: Better than 1.0uV for 10dB S = N/N.
Selectivity: 20KHz @ 10dB.
Programming: Crystal.

Modes: Narrow AM.
Number of channels: 6.
Display: LED lamp.
Search: No.
Priority: No.
Delay: Fixed.
Lockout: No.
Power source: 9V PP3.
Audio out: Not stated.
External connections: Antenna (BNC) and external speaker/ headphones, 9V DC.
Manual tuning knob: No.
Dimensions: 62x115x28mm.
Additional features: Can be manually set to any one channel. 9V NiCad battery with charger is available as an optional extra.
Comments: Very compact pocket portable.

Model: Signal R535.
Type: Base/mobile.

Receiver type: Not stated.
Coverage: 108—143MHz, 220—380MHz.
Quoted sensitivity: Not stated.
Selectivity: Not stated.
Modes: AM only.
Search: User defined limits.
Memory channels: 60.

Programming: Up/down push button.
Priority: No.
Delay: Yes.
Lockout: Individual channels or groups.
Display: Matrix LCD (Alphanumeric).
Power source: 13.8V DC.
External connections: Extension speaker, power, antenna.
Additional features: Supplied with power chord, telescopic antenna and mobile mounting bracket. Circuitry includes a noise blanker to reduce pulse type (vehicle ignition) interference.
Comments: A specialised airband receiver which replaces the R532. Optional extras include a carry case, NiCad pack and charger and AC power supply pack. A fairly tedious type of programming is involved but the set is highly spoken of by airband enthusiasts.

Model: Sony Air-7.

Type: Hand-held portable.

Receiver: Synthesised double Superhetrodyne.

Coverage: 150—2194KHz AM, 76—108MHz WBFM, 108—136MHz AM & 144—174MHz NBFM.

Programming: Keypad.

Modes: AM, WBFM, NBFM automatically selected according to band.

Number of channels: 10 per band.

Display: Liquid Crystal Display (LCD).

Search: Bandsearch only.

Delay: Yes.

Priority: Yes.

Power source: 6V DC from 4 x AA cells. Rechargeable packs, AC and 12V vehicle adaptors available as an optional extra.

Audio out: 400mW at 8 Ohms.

External connections: 6V DC, earphone, antenna (BNC).

Dimensions: 90W x 179H x 50D (mm). Weighs 600g.

Comments: Bulky, heavy, limited coverage and expensive. However, airband fans say it performs superbly and I'm told the AGC (very important with AM) is excellent.

Model: Sony PRO-80.

Type: Handheld.

Receiver type: Synthesised double superhetrodyne.

Coverage: 150KHz—108MHz, 115—223MHz (using plug-in converter which connects to the antenna socket).

Quoted sensitivity: Not stated.

Selectivity: Not stated.

Modes: AM, FM, WBFM & SSB but AM/FM is not user selectable on VHF.

Search: Between user defined limits.

Memory channels: 40.

Programming: Keypad.

Priority: Yes.

Delay: No.

Display: LCD.

Power source: 6V from 4xAA cells. Rechargeable cells and AC and 12v DC adaptors available as extras.

External connections: 6v DC, earphone and antenna (TNC).

Additional features: Supplied with plug-in VHF adaptor (not shown in photograph) and helical antenna.

Comments: Similar in shape size and weight to the Air-7 and also expensive. Although the PRO-80 performs well, is built to Sony's usual high standard and includes LW, MW and full HF coverage, it does not include UHF. The VHF coverage is provided by a plug-in adaptor which seems a bit of a scruffy afterthought on the part of the designer.

Model: WIN 108.

Type: Handheld portable.

Receiver type: Not stated.

Coverage: 108—135.975MHz.

Quoted sensitivity: Not stated.

Selectivity: Not stated.

Modes: AM only.

Search: Between user defined limits (25KHz step rates allow for future re-allocating of airband channels).

Memory channels: 20 (2 x 10 and only 10 can be used at any one time).

Programming: Keypad.

Priority: Channel 0.

Delay: Yes.

Display: LCD.

Power source: 6V DC internal NiCads or AA dry cells or 6V DC external.

External connections: Earphone, 6V DC, antenna (BNC).

Comments: A scanner that has received mixed reactions. Some owners speak highly of it but some magazine reviews have been critical with

claims that the keyboard is flimsy and difficult to operate and sensitivity could be better on a set designed solely for AM mode.

Model: Yaesu-Musen FRG-9600.

Importer/Agent: South Midlands Communications.

Type: Synthesised base/mobile.

Receiver: Triple/double/single (video) conversion.

Coverage: 60—905MHz (no gaps).

Quoted sensitivity: FMN 0.5uV (12dB SINAD)
FMW 1.0uV (12dB SINAD)
AMN 1.0uV (10dB S + S/N)
AMW 1.5uV (10dB S + S/N)
SSB 1.0uV (15dB S + S/N)

Selectivity: @ 3dB FMN 15KHz
FMW 180KHz
AMN 2.4KHz
AMW 6.0KHz
SSB 2.4KHz

Programming: Keypad.

Modes: Wide and narrow FM, Wide and narrow AM, SSB (up to 460MHz only) and NTSC format video with optional adaptor.

Number of channels: 100.

Display: Green fluorescent.

Search: Yes. 100Hz + 1/5/10/12/100KHz.

Priority: Yes.

Delay: No.

Lockout: Yes. Required channels are programmed for scan.

Power source: 12V DC or 240V AC via optional external adaptor. Memory backup is via rechargeable lithium cell.

Audio out: 1 Watt.

External connections: Antenna, video out (optional), computer interface external speaker.

Manual tuning knob: Yes. Facility to transfer tuned frequency to memory and bring frequency from memory to provide a start point for manual tuning.

Dimensions: 180x80x220mm.

Comments: Well built but it has a strange feature in that after about ten seconds it resumes scanning even if the station it stopped on is still transmitting. Various computer interfaces are available. R. Withers Communications supply a re-vamped version with better sensitivity and UHF up to 950MHz and, if required, an internal adaptor to give coverage from 100KHz—60MHz. They can also supply a PAL video adaptor.

Accessories

Listed here are some of the more exotic accessories that can be used with scanners. I have not included smaller items such as headphones, loudspeakers, slide-mounts, etc as these are generally available from a wide variety of sources including electronic hobby shops, CB dealers, etc.

Product: Revco AP2 masthead amplifier.

Distributor: Garex.

Description: A masthead pre-amplifier that gives around 18dB of gain over the band 20—700MHz with slightly less gain over an extended range of 10—1000MHz. Noise figures are not quoted but the unit is very compact and has PL259 connections at either end. This means that the amplifier will easily fit inside the mounting pole of an aerial like a discone.

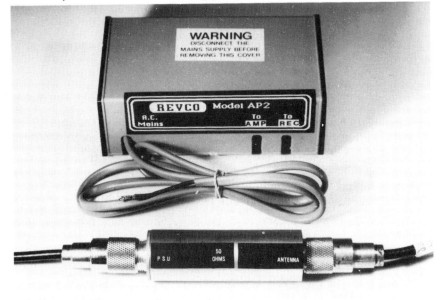

Comments: Very easy to fit. Cut into the aerial downlead just below the antenna. Fit PL259s to the cable ends and plug up to the pre-amp. If the amplifier cannot go inside the mounting pole then some kind of weather proofing will be needed such as self-amalgamating tape. At the scanner end the aerial is connected into the power supply box and a short lead is fitted to connect to the antenna socket of the scanner.

Kuranishi converters

Kuranishi converters for both HF and UHF are designed for use with the FRG-9600 scanner but there is no reason to believe that they will not work equally well with other equipment which tunes the required range.

The HF converter (model FC965DX) is a simple unit which provides HF coverage from 20KHz to 60MHz when the scanner is tuned to the range 60.020—120MHz. The 8V DC power supply for the unit is taken from the supply socket on the rear of the 9600 and so if the converter is used for a different scanner then obviously a supply will need to be arranged. No figures are quoted for the performance of the equipment and obviously that performance will be determined to a large degree by the scanner itself. It should be noted that this convertor will not, for instance, work very well with a scanner such as the AOR AR2002 as the IF filters are far too wide for HF coverage. On the other hand, it may be used to good advantage with an Icom R7000 where narrow filters are available for AM and SSB.

Kuranishi HF and UHF converters for the Yaesu FRG-9600

The UHF converter (model FC-1300) is designed to provide coverage of the band 905—1300MHz when the scanner is tuned between 505—900MHz. Again this converter should be able to work with any scanner that can cover that range. The converter requires 12V DC to operate and when switched off the circuit is bypassed for normal scanner operation.

JIL R. F. Adaptors

A range of frequency converters designed primarily for use with the SX400 Scanner but the UK Agents (Garex) say they can be used with other scanners.

RF8014: This unit covers 800MHz to 1.4GHz. Its IF output lies in the range 300—500MHz.

RF5080: This unit covers 500—800MHz. Its IF output lies in the range 200—300MHz.

Both units are controlled by a switching signal from the SX-400 which switches the adaptor into circuit when it is required (there is no need to start plugging or unplugging aerial and connector leads).

Connections include a 7-pin DIN plug connection to the scanner's control circuit and 12V DC supply input.

Both converters are supplied with connecting leads, aerial plug adaptors and power supply leads and both can be brought under external computer control when the SX-400 is used in that way.

RF1030: This is an up-converter which turns the SX-400 into a fully synthesised HF communications receiver/scanner. It covers the frequency range 100KHz to 20MHz and has additional control circuitry as follows: Fine tuning (Delta tuning), USB, LSB and CW modes, noise blanker, AF gain, RF attenuator and squelch. The front panel also carries indicators to show band, mode and power. All operation is under full control of the main scanner.

On the back panel of the adaptor are sockets for both HF and the normal VHF/UHF aerial (automatically switched), interconnection to the scanner and 10.7MHz IF input. This latter socket can be hooked up to the 10.7MHz output of the scanner to give SSB operation on UHF and VHF. The adaptor contains its own independent audio output and again the whole unit can be brought under external computer control via the SX-400.

ACB300: This is an antenna control box for use with the JIL adaptors and it is a necessary accessory if more than one adaptor is going to be used. It takes the input from the normal scanner aerial plus the outputs from the adaptors and switches the appropriate circuit to the scanner. It is controlled by the SX-400's circuit. It requires 12V DC input.

HO-1: This is a frequency converter which enables coverage of the band 96—108MHz. Its output is in the range 26—38MHz. It was originally designed to fill-in the gap on the SX-200 but should work with any scanner which can cover the range of its output. It has a BNC antenna socket and flying leads terminated in a Motorola plug. Power requirements are 12V DC @ 30mA.

Antennae

I do not propose here to go into a long review of all the antennas available such as dipoles, whips, discones, etc as they are available from a wide range of sources. Instead, what are presented here are a few of the more unusual antennas which may be of interest to scanner users.

Produce: Radac Antenna

Manufacturer: Revco (available from Garex).

Description: This is what is known as a 'Nest of dipoles' type of antenna. It is quite an old idea which has been re-vamped to meet the needs of scanner users. In theory it provides reception on six bands which are determined by the length of each of the individual dipole sections. The manufacturers say that for those six bands, aerial gain will be better than a discone. Elements can be anywhere in the range 25—500MHz.

Comments: I have had several arguments with scanner buffs over the virtues of the Radac when compared with a discone. I have never been a discone lover and believe that manufacturers make some quite outrageous claims for the performance of these devices (claiming 20 to 1300MHz coverage for instance). My own experience with the Radac, which has been purely subjective, is that on the selected bands performance is better than a discone. If the bands are evenly spread across the spectrum then even at midway between bands performance is usable, albeit a compromise. I've owned several discones and found all

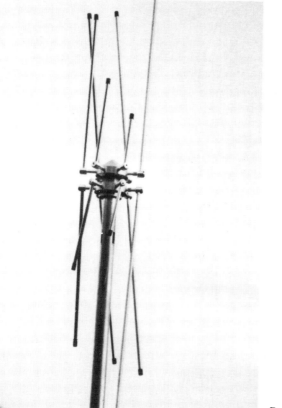

Radac Antenna

of them to have performance that falls off rapidly above 200MHz. I suspect that although the theoretical VSWR of such devices remains relatively constant across the range some other factor, possibly radiation angle, does not. I personally prefer the nest of dipoles but will concede that the scanner owner who wants to constantly hunt all VHF/UHF frequencies may be better off with a discone.

Earlier versions of the Radac suffered from the longer elements working loose with such things as wind movement but Revco have now solved this problem by using double grub screw locking.

Product: ARA 500 Active Antenna.
Manufacturer: Dressler.
Description: Broadband antenna with built-in signal amplifier.
Gain: 50—650MHz 17dB typical.
    650—950MHz 10dB typical.

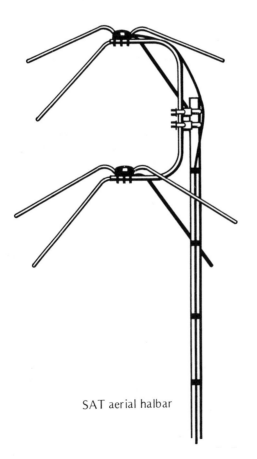

SAT aerial halbar

Noise: 1dB @ 50—180MHz —1.5dB below 300MHz — 2.0dB below 350MHZ — 2.7dB below 400MHz — 3.0dB below 500MHz — 3.8dB below 650MHz — 4—6dB below 950MHz.

Intercept: The third order intercept point is quoted as + 18dBm.

Comments: To look at it consists of a tube with bracket at the base for mounting to a mast. A broadband amplifier is built into the tube but what kind of antenna system is built into the device is not stated.

Product: I.T/u and I.T/tn Satellite antennas.

Manufacturer: Halbar.

Type: Crossed dipoles.

Description: I.T/u Covers 145.825MHz (UOSATS 1 & 2) with left-hand circular polarisation. I.T/tn covers 137.5 weather satellite band with right hand polarisation. Both antennas have a built-in phasing harness but the purchaser must provide his own mounting mast which is not included in the price. A mast-head pre-amplifier is available for both versions and can be specified at the time of ordering so that the device can be built into the antenna.

Comments: The price of the pre-amplifier does not include a power supply. Halbar are able to supply all the equipment needed to set up a complete weather station, including receiver, digitizer and software for the BBC-B computer.

Product: Diamond CLP5130-2.

Type: Log periodic.

Description: A 20 element Log periodic antenna with coverage from 105MHz to 1300MHz. The gain is quoted as 11—13dB with a front to back ratio of 15dB. The antenna has a width of 1.4 metres and is 1.4 metres long. VSWR across the range is quoted as 2:1 and terminations are via an N-socket.

Product: Diamond CLP5130-1.

Type: Log periodic.

Description: A wider band version of the above antenna covering 50—1300MHz. A 24 element unit which is 3 metres wide and 2 metres long, otherwise the specifications are similar.

Product: Diamond D707.

Type: Multiband pole.

Description: The antenna consists of a slim pole 95cms long which contains a broadband 20dB gain signal pre-amplifier. However, no details are given of the type of elements employed nor the performance across the range which is quoted as 2—1500MHz. The antenna is supplied with a small power unit which sends voltage for the pre-amplifier up the coaxial feeder cable and some provision is made in the interface to vary the gain of the system.

Product: Diamond D505.

Type: Multiband mobile antenna.

Description: Essentially a mobile version of the above antenna with the same specifications. The unit consists of a mobile mounting whip with two loading coils and built-in pre-amplifier. The antenna is 80cms long.

Sandpiper antennae

Sandpiper manufacture an extremely wide range of antennae and it would be impossible to provide a complete list of their products. However, I would mention a few of their products which are of particular interest to scanner owners. First, they manufacture log periodics, discones and nests of dipoles (several versions of each covering different frequency ranges) as well as several versions of a multi-band mobile antenna which can also be used as a base unit for anyone who cannot mount a discone.

They can also supply high gain colinears for air and marine bands and the same bands are covered by a range of helical antennae for handsets. Because Sandpiper manufacture these products on a sort of modular basis they can supply helicals for instance, for any band with any type of plug (including right angle connections). Their range stretches to yagis and dipoles for virtually any frequency and again, because of the method of manufacture involved, costs are virtually the same as for an off-the-shelf product.

Should you want to build your own antenna then Sandpiper can also supply both aluminium and fibreglass tubing as well as connector blocks and all the usual fittings. Again the range is so vast it is impossible to cover it here and you should contact them (address at the back of the book) and get a copy of their lists.

Nevada

Nevada can supply a range of plug-in antennae for portable hand-helds. These include UHF and Airband helicals and telescopics terminated in BNC, TNC or N-type plugs. Nevada also supply the Weltz/Royale discone under their own brand name, model WB1300.

Butternut

The Butternut SC-3000 antenna imported by Uppington Tele-Radio of Bristol (also available from other dealers) is an unusual alternative to the discone. The antenna consists of a vertical pole with what are known as 'Trombone' phasing sections. Coverage is from 30—512MHz and gain is quoted as unity at low band, up to 3dB at VHF and up to 7dB at UHF (although no reference is quoted for these gain figures). The length is 11 foot and the antenna is supplied with a ground-plane.

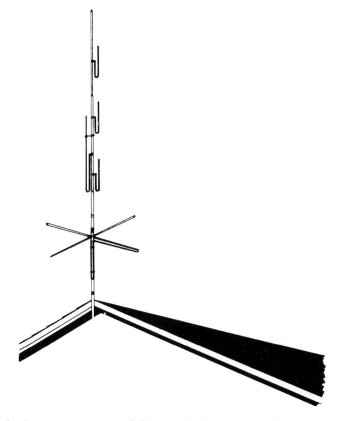

I have had no experience of this particular antenna but suspect that performance is probably similar to the nest of dipoles type where performance tends to peak on some bands.

10 UK Scanner and accessory manufacturers, importers, distributors and dealers

This list is restricted to those firms offering full mail order facilities. To locate retailers in your own area try the yellow pages of the telephone directory under headings such as 'Communications', 'Amateur Radio', 'C.B. Radio', etc.

AIRCASTLE PRODUCTS
P.O. Box 78
Bournemouth BH1 4SP
Tel: 0202-632040
Computer control systems & software

AIR SUPPLY
83B High Street
Yeadon
Leeds LS19 7TA
Tel: 0532-509581
Scanners, Aero charts, antennae

ALAN HOOKER ELECTRONICS
42 Nethernall Road
Doncaster
Tel: 0302-25690
Scanners, antennae and Fax/data decoders

AMATEUR RADIO COMMUNICATIONS LIMITED
38 Bridge Street
Earlestown
Newton-le-Willows
Merseyside WA12 9BA
Tel: 09252-29881
Scanners, internal and external HF adaptors, antennae, books

AMMCOMM
373 Uxbridge Road
London W3 9RN
Tel: 01-992 5765
Scanners, antennae

A.R.E COMMUNICATIONS LIMITED
6 Royal Parade
Hangar Lane
Ealing
London W5A 1ET
Tel: 01-991 2565
Scanners (special VHF/UHF/HF version of Icom R7000), books,
pre-amps, antennae

THE AVIATION HOBBY CENTRE
1st Floor
Main Terminal
Birmingham Intl Airport
W. Midlands B26 3QJ
Tel: 021-742 0424
Scanners, antennae and books

ARROW ELECTRONICS LIMITED
5 The Street
Hatfield Peverel
Essex CM3 2EJ
Tel: 0245-381673
Scanners, antennae

BREDHURST ELECTRONICS LIMITED
High Street
Handcross
West Sussex RH17 6BW
Tel: 0444-400786
Scanners, base and mobile antennae and books

CIRKIT DISTRIBUTION LIMITED
Park Lane
Broxbourne
Herts EN10 7NQ
Tel: 0992-444111
Scanners, books, RF plugs, sockets and components

COMPONENT CENTRE
7 Langley Road
Watford
Hertfordshire WD1 3PS
Tel: 0923-245335
Scanners, antennae

DATONG ELECTRONICS LIMITED
Clayton Wood Close
West Park
Leeds LS16 6QE
Tel: 0532-744822
HF adaptors

DEWSBURY ELECTRONICS
176 Lower High Street
Stourbridge
West Midlands
Tel: 0384-390063, 371228
Scanners, antennae

DRESSLER COMMUNICATIONS LIMITED
191 Francis Road
Leyton
London E10 6NQ
Tel: 01-558 0845, 01-556 1415
Scanners, antennae

ELLIOTT ELECTRONICS
26/28 Braunstone Gate
Leicester
Tel: 0533-553293
Scanners, antennae, pre-amps, books

FLIGHTDECK
58-62 Lower Hillgate
Stockport
Cheshire SK1 3AN
Tel: 061-480 8080
Scanners, aero charts and books, antennae

GAREX ELECTRONICS
7 Norvic Road
Marsworth
Tring
Hertfordshire HP23 4LS
Tel: 0296 668684
Scanners, antennae, books, computer control systems, converters, weather satellite systems, pre-amps, direction finding equipment

HALBAR LIMITED
Unit 1
Bury Walk
Bedford MK41 0DU
Tel: 0234 44720
Satellite aerials

ICOM (UK) LIMITED
Sea Street
Herne Bay
Kent CT6 8LD
Tel: 0227 363859
Scanners, antennae

ICS ELECTRONICS LIMITED
P.O. Box 2
Arundel
West Sussex BN18 0NX
Tel: 0243-65655
Fax and multi-mode data decoders.

INTERBOOKS
8 Abbot Street
Perth PH2 0EB
Scotland
Tel: 0738-30707
Wide range of books and frequency lists

JAVIATION
Carlton Works
Carlton Street
Bradford
West Yorkshire BD7 1DA
Tel: 0274-732146
Scanners, antennae, aviation charts, frequency lists, pre-amps, airband crystals

JOHNSONS SHORTWAVE RADIO
43 Friar Street
Worcester WR1 2NA
Tel: 0905-25740
Scanners, antennae and PSU's

LINK ELECTRONICS
228 Lincoln Road
Peterborough
Tel: 0733-45731
Scanners, antennae

LINKS COMMUNICATIONS
Crossways Centre
Braye Rd
Vale
Guernsey C.I.
Tel: 0481-48360
Scanners and antennae (VAT free export)

LOWE ELECTRONICS LIMITED
Chesterfield Road
Matlock
Derbyshire DE4 5LE
Tel: 0629-2817, 2430, 4057, 4995
Scanners, antennae

MAPLIN ELECTRONIC SUPPLIES LIMITED
P.O. Box 3
Rayleigh
Essex SS6 8LR
Tel: 0702-552991
Wide range of plugs, connectors, power supplies, Ni-Cads,
books, etc.

MGR SERVICES
48 Shrewsbury Road
Oxton
Birkenhead L43 2HZ
Tel: 051-653-3437
Scanners, antennae

NEVADA COMMUNICATIONS
189 London Road
North End
Portsmouth PO2 9AE
Tel: 0705-662145
Scanners (main agents for Uniden Bearcat and Black Jaguar), books, antennae, pre-amps

PHOTO ACOUSTICS LIMITED
58 High Street
Newport Pagnell
Buckinghamshire MK16 8AQ
Tel: 0908-610625
Scanners, antennae

PW PUBLISHING LIMITED
Enefco House
The Quay
Poole
Dorset BH15 1PP
Tel: 0102-678558
Large range of books (Short Wave Magazine has regular coverage of scanners)

RADCOM ELECTRONICS
Unit 4
Albert Quay
Cork City
Tel: 021-632725, 021-313611
Scanners, antennae, pre-amps

RADIO AMATEUR SUPPLIES (NOTTINGHAM)
3 Farndon Green
Woollaton Park
Nottingham NH8 1DU
Tel: 0602-280267
Scanners, antennae

RADIO SHACK LIMITED
188 Broadhurst Gardens
London NW6 3AY
Tel: 01-624 7174
Scanners, antennae, fax decoders and books

RAYCOM COMMUNICATION SYSTEMS LIMITED
International House
963 Wolverhampton Road
Oldbury
West Midlands B69 4RJ
Tel: 021-544 6767
Scanners (Uniden/Bearcat importers), antennae

REG WARD & COMPANY LIMITED
1 Western Parade
West Street
Axminster
Devon EX13 5NY
Tel: 0297-34918
Scanners, antennae

REVCO ELECTRONICS LIMITED
Station Yard
South Brent
South Devon TQ10 9AL
Tel: 0364-73394
Scanners, antennae (manufacturers), pre-amps, direction finding
equipment

SANDPIPER COMMUNICATIONS
Pentwyn House
Penyard
Llwydcoed
Aberdare
Mid Glamorgan CF44 0TU
Tel: 0685-870425
Scanners and antennae (manufacturers)

SEAWARD ELECTRONICS
Kings Hill Industrial Estate
Bude
Cornwall
Tel: 0288-55998
Scanners, antennae and accessories

SISKIN ELECTRONICS
Southampton Road
Hythe
Southampton SO4 6WQ
Tel: 0703-849962
Scanners, antennae

SOUTH MIDLANDS COMMUNICATIONS LIMITED
SM House
School Close
Chandlers Ford Industrial Estate
Eastleigh
Hampshire SO5 3BY
Tel: 0703-255111
(branches in Leeds, Chesterfield, Buckley, Jersey, Bangor,
Birmingham and Axminster).
Scanners (official agents for Yaesu), antennae, converters

STEPHENS JAMES LIMITED
47 Warrington Road
Leigh
Lancashire WN7 3AE
Tel: 0942-676790
Scanners, antennae and fitting kits

TANDY CORPORATION (BRANCH UK)
Tameway Tower
Bridge Street
Walsall
West Midlands WS1 1LA
Sole suppliers of Realistic scanners. Tandy shops are located throughout
Britain, check your area telephone directory for the nearest branch.

UPPINGTON LIMITED
12-14 Pennywell Road
Bristol
BS5 0TJ
Tel: 0272-557732
Scanners and antennae (including Butternut types)

WATERS & STANTON
18-20 Main Road
Hockley
Essex SS5 4QS
Tel: 0702-206835, 204965
Scanners, pre-amps, converters, books (list publishers), antennae
(including log periodics)

Organisations
AMATEUR RADIO

THE RADIO SOCIETY OF GREAT BRITAIN
Lambda House, Cranborne Road, Potters Bar,
Hertfordshire EN6 3JW
Telephone: 0707 59015

MARINE, LAND MOBILE, ETC, GOVERNMENT
REGULATORY BODY

THE DEPARTMENT OF TRADE AND INDUSTRY
Radio Regulatory Division (R1), Waterloo Bridge House,
Waterloo Road, London SE1 8UA

Scanners 2 is the perfect match to the book you are reading now. It is not just a revised version of *Scanners 1* but an entirely separate book that goes into the subject of the more advanced scanner user and also covers VHF/UHF monitor receivers. Scanners 2 is also an international edition.

Here are some of the subjects that are covered:

Modifications: Simultaneous AM/FM for the SX-200 and Bearcat 220FB.

Common faults: SX-200 (various improvements), Bearcat 220 (power supply), AOR 2001 (Off frequency), etc.

DIY accessories: Active antenna, SX-200 front panel S-Meter, B.F.O., broadband and narrow band masthead amplifiers, power supplies, auto NiCad charger, 12V to 6V or 9V adaptor for portables and automatic recording switch.

Project: Build a 10 channel crystal controlled pocket or mobile scanner. Easy to build VHF/FM design that uses parts available from regular component suppliers.

Computer control: A detailed look at the advantages of using a personal computer to control a scanner (AOR 2002, ICOM, SX-400, etc.)

Dxing: Using your scanner for long distance reception. How to recognise the signs that a lift is on, where to tune and hear stations from as far away as the USA under the right conditions. List of VHF broadcast stations,beacons, repeaters, etc.

Spectrum: Full international spectrum allocations for all three ITU regions from 26—1300MHz.

Callsigns: Full list of International, Air and Marine Callsigns and registrations.

Airports: Spot frequencies of the world's major airports.

LOGBOOK

Mem No.	Fcy MHz	Mode	Station	Notes
01				
02				
03				
04				
05				
06				
07				
08				
09				
10				
11				
12				
13				
14				
15				
16				
17				
18				
19				
20				

LOGBOOK

Mem No.	Fcy MHz	Mode	Station	Notes
21				
22				
23				
24				
25				
26				
27				
28				
29				
30				
31				
32				
33				
34				
35				
36				
37				
38				
39				
40				

LOGBOOK

Mem No.	Fcy MHz	Mode	Station	Notes
01				
02				
03				
04				
05				
06				
07				
08				
09				
10				
11				
12				
13				
14				
15				
16				
17				
18				
19				
20				

LOGBOOK

Mem No.	Fcy MHz	Mode	Station	Notes

Index